EDEN AGAIN:

HOPE IN THE
MARSHES OF IRAQ

≋ PRAISE FOR
EDEN AGAIN: HOPE IN THE MARSHES OF IRAQ

"The *ahwar* (marshlands) of southern Iraq represent one of [Iraq's] most valuable natural treasures. Dr. Alwash has portrayed the environment of the *ahwar* and its people with sensitive and accurate detail, providing an authoritative account of how the marshes were destroyed under Saddam Hussein's regime and then restored through the spontaneous actions of the local community. In contrast to the stories of sectarian violence that fill the world's newspapers, this is a tale of successful cooperation across all of Iraq's religious, political, and class sectors—a tale of Shia and Sunni, Kurd and Arab, male and female, destitute and wealthy, peasant and professor—joined with the assistance of Americans, Italians, British, Canadians, and Japanese, all reaching out to help one other, in a true story of the possibility of intercultural harmony in the rich and complex tapestry of modern Iraq. Every library should have a copy of this important book."

—*Dr. Ayad Allawi,* Prime Minister of Iraq, 2003-05

"In a world where paradoxically nature is being destroyed at an ever faster pace in spite of our deeper understanding of its crucial values to us, there are few success stories more inspiring than those of restoring nature to its original splendour. Loaded with symbolism, historical, cultural and biological values like few other places, the restoration of the vast Mesopotamian marshes in Iraq, illustrated so beautifully in *Eden Again*, provides the hope and the inspiration for the ultimate challenge—and splendid opportunity—to live in harmony with nature."

—*Marco Lambertini,* CEO, BirdLife International

"There are three important reasons why I recommend the book *Eden Again: Hope in the Marshes of Iraq* as essential reading for all Americans. The first reason is to correct the misperceptions of many American people and the media about the land and people of Iraq. Images portrayed in the American news are of strange, unhappy or frightening people associated with terrorism and random acts of violence. This book brings alive the humor, intelligence, dedication, generosity, and commitment of the Iraqi scientists, engineers, students, and ordinary people who strive to restore water and livelihood to the ancient Mesopotamian Marshes. Second, this is an inspiring tale of Suzie and Azzam Alwash as they founded Iraq's first environmental organization, Nature Iraq. The book allows readers to experience their passionate love of the marshes, their sacrifices and successes, and the satisfaction gained from working with dynamic Iraqis to rejuvenate the marshes and the people who suffered terribly under the Baathist regime. And lastly, this book is a story of hope, of individuals who have made a positive difference in revitalizing the marsh ecosystem, the indigenous Marsh Arab lifestyle, and future Iraqi communities. This is an inspirational and well-written story of hard work, sacrifice, and service."

—*Dr. Michelle Stevens,* Executive Director, Hima Mesopotamia

"In 1964 Wilfred Thesiger brought to life the fascinating culture and mysterious world of the Marsh Arabs or "Madan" of the Mesopotamian Marshes of Iraq. Thirty years later the culture and the marshes were nearly destroyed by the Hussein regime. In *Eden Again* by Suzanne Alwash we now have the inside story of how the marshes were drained and partially restored, and how some of the Madan survived both environmental genocide and untold political hardships to return to the marshes following their reflooding. Having dedicated the last ten years of their lives to try to and save the marshes and this ancient culture has given Alwash and her husband Azzam unique insights into the political, social, and scientific struggles that have gripped the region. More importantly their scientific and environmental field work in Iraq has given us a view of how restoration can be accomplished under often perilous political and seemingly insurmountable environmental conditions. Alwash gives the reader a rare first-hand view of the trials and tribulations of doing marsh ecosystem restoration work in a war zone filled with civic disorder, tribal conflicts, and limited water supplies due to drought and regional water conflicts. Like the phoenix, the marshes have risen from the ashes of fire and this book recounts how 'getting the water right' provides hope for the future."

—*Dr. Curtis J. Richardson*
Professor and Director Duke University Wetland Center
Nicholas School of the Environment

"This highly readable story of one of humanity's great wetland civilizations is a dramatic, captivating tale. Thoroughly researched and based on first-hand information, Suzanne Alwash provides an all-round account of southern Iraq's marshlands—from the resilience of the age-old culture of the Marsh Arabs and their enchanting water-world with its spectacular birdlife and rich fisheries to the battle for water in the Middle East and the intrigues of international development assistance. *Eden Again* provides a stunning testament to nature's incredible capacity to self-heal in one of the planet's most disturbed environments. Over the past decade, the Alwashes have been on the frontline battle to bring the marshes back to life and have privileged insights on the challenges and opportunities faced. If the promised *Eden Again* is not to fade into mirage, reaching a water sharing agreement between the Tigris-Euphrates riparian countries and preparing for the dire impacts of climate change are key to securing a sustainable future for the marshlands, its people, and exceptional wildlife.

—*Hassan Partow,* Program Manager,
United Nations Environmental Program

"Few of us find the perfect book to engage students in multi-disciplinary learning about our favorite topic. But I did. The book is *Eden Again...* and the topic is wetlands. Suzanne Alwash is not just an author with extensive knowledge of the history, devastation, and potential rebirth of the Mesopotamian wetlands; she is also a scientist who understands wetlands and a heroine who has dedicated much of her career to conserving and restoring a wetlands that once covered over 6,000 square miles. Alwash tells the many interwoven stories about geography, ecology, livelihoods, politics, war, and culture with a sound factual basis gained from scientific research and interviews with victims who survived Saddam Hussein's wrath. Her expert writing holds our attention and compels us to care. *Eden Again* is a perfect book for students in my interdisciplinary undergraduate course, Plants and Humans, and my advanced course in Adaptive Restoration. No one should ignore this ongoing struggle to restore the Mesopotamian Marshes and a way of living that persisted for millennia. And all who aim for global sustainability need to understand the many critical services that wetlands provide for human well-being."

—*Dr. Joy Zedler,* Aldo Leopold Chair of Restoration Ecology,
University of Wisconsin-Madison

"Suzanne Alwash has provided a vivid and elegantly written account of the struggle for survival, against all odds, of the ancient Mesopotamian marshes—domain of an extraordinary ecosystem, history, and culture that have survived for millennia, world-famous as the "cradle of civilization" and legendary as the alleged site of the Biblical Garden of Eden. The book weaves together environmental knowledge and scientific data with the colorful personal tales of individuals, chief among them the author and Azzam Alwash, who were captivated by the wetlands and labored tirelessly before and after 2003, sometimes in great danger, to overcome the political and environmental challenges to the restoration of the endangered marshlands of Iraq."

—*Rend al-Rahim,* Iraq Ambassador to
the United States of America, 2003-04

"This book tells a story that is unknown to most, and should be of interest to all."

—*Jay Nordlinger*, Senior Editor, National Review

EDEN AGAIN:

HOPE IN THE
MARSHES OF IRAQ

SUZANNE ALWASH

TABLET HOUSE PUBLISHING
2013

ISBN (hardcover edition): 978-0-98886514-2-5
ISBN (softcover edition): 978-0-9886514-3-2

Library of Congress Control Number (hardcover edition): 2012954606
Library of Congress Control Number (softcover edition): 2012955880

Library of Congress Cataloging-in-Publication Data:

    Alwash, Suzanne.
    Eden Again : Hope in the Marshes of Iraq / by Suzanne Alwash.
    p. cm.
    Includes bibliographical references and index.

    1. Natural history—Iraq. 2. Marshes—Iraq.
    3. Ecology—Iraq. 4. Social ecology—Iraq.
    5. Iraq—Civilization. 6. Iraq—History.   I. Title.

    QH193.I7A49 2013   508.567'5
                    QBI12-600232

First published in 2013

Tablet House Publishing, 1770 Catlin Street, Fullerton CA 92833
www.tablethousepublishing.com

Printed in Hong Kong by Elegance Printing

Cover and interior design by Tania Baban-Natal, Conflux Press

To my daughters,
Hannah & Norah

and in memory of
Jawad Mahdi Alwash

❧ CONTENTS

☙ LIST OF FIGURES

☙ LIST OF TABLES

✌ LIST OF PHOTOGRAPHS

✍ ABBREVIATIONS AND ACRONYMS

AMAR	Assisting Marsh Arabs and Refugees
Aus-AID	Australian Government Overseas Aid Agency
bcm	billion cubic meters
CBD	Convention on Biodiversity
CIA	Central Intelligence Agency
CIDA	Canadian Internationa l Development Agency
cms	cubic centimeters per second
COP	Ramsar's Conference of Parties
CPA	Coalition Provisional Authority
CSIRO	Australian Commonwealth Scientific and Industrial Research Organization
CRIM	Center for Restoration of the Iraqi Marshlands
DAI	Development Alternatives International, Inc.
DFID	United Kingdom Department for International Development
FAO	Food and Agriculture Organization of the United Nations
GAP	Southeastern Anatolia Project
GIS	Geographic Information Systems
IAEC	Iraq Atomic Energy Commission
IBA	Important Bird Area
IETC	International Environmental Technology Center
IMELS	Italian Ministry of the Environment, Land, and Sea
IMOS	Iraqi Marshland Observation System
IUCN	International Union for Conservation of Nature
JICA	Japan International Cooperation Agency
KBA	Key Biodiversity Area
MODIS	Moderate Resolution Imaging Spectroradiometer
MoE	Iraq Ministry of the Environment
MoSMA	Iraq Minister of State for Marshland Affairs
MoWR	Iraq Ministry of Water Resources
NASA	National Aeronautics and Space Administration
ORHA	Office of Reconstruction and Humanitarian Assistance
RO	Reverse Osmosis
UNEP	United Nations Environmental Program Organization
UNESCO	United Nations Educational, Scientific, and Cultural Organization
UNICEF	United Nations International Children's Fund
USAID	United States Agency for International Development

❧ GLOSSARY OF ARABIC WORDS

abaya   a black cloak worn by many Islamic women in Iraq; it does not cover the face

ahwar   Arabic word for marshlands

balam   a large, flat-bottomed wooden canoe, generally about 35 feet long

bata'ih   Arabic word for lagoon, the term for the marshlands during medieval times

bizz   a species of fish also known as mangar or Tigris Salmon (*Luciobarbus esocinus*)

bunni   a species of fish (*Mesopotamichthys sharpeyi*)

dibbis   date syrup

chalabiya   a small raft used by children in the marshes

dishdasha   traditional men's garment, a loose cotton shirt extending to the ankles

fatwa   a legal opinion or decree handed down by an Islamic religious authority

fellah   a peasant farmer

fedayeen   insurgents

gattan   a species of fish (*Luciobarbus xanthopterus*)

ghaymer   a soft fresh cheese made from water buffalo milk, similar to cream cheese

halal   lawful or permissible under Islam

haram   forbidden or prohibited under Islam

hashish   new, green shoots of reeds usually cut for water buffalo fodder

hauwa   a method of night fishing

hillawi   a method of fishing using coarsely-woven material

ishan   an area of slightly higher elevation within the marshlands, a low broad hill

jirri   a species of catfish (*Silurius triostegus*)

ma'dan   the people of the marshes; also used as a pejorative term.

majnoon   the Arabic word for crazy

masgouf	a method for cooking fish impaled on sticks over an open fire
mashuf	a narrow wooden canoe with upturned ends
mataur	a flat, rectangular boat, just large enough for one man to lie prone while bird hunting
mudhif	a barrel-vaulted guest house built of bundled reeds and reed mats
nakhla	date palm
numi basra	dried lime
peshmerga	a Kurdish resistance fighter or guerrilla
sabr	the Arabic word for patience
sbour	a species of fish, also known as the Hilsa or Indian Shad (*Tenualosa ilisha*)
shabout	a species of fish (*Tor grypus*)
Shamal	a wind blowing from the northwest, usually during the summer, bringing sandstorms
Sharqi	a wind blowing from the southeast, usually during the spring and fall
shatt	Arabic word for river or canal
shawiyya	nomadic shepherds
shillik	a species of fish (*Aspius vorax*)
tarada	a war canoe, shaped like a *mashuf* but around 35 feet long
tehela	a large raft of floating reeds, torn from the substrate during storms
werda	a species of bird, also known as the African Darter
zobaidy	a species of fish (*Pampus argenteus*)
zurri	a general term for a small fish

ABOUT THE AUTHOR

Suzanne Reynolds Alwash was raised on a small family farm nestled amongst the thickets along Cottonwood Creek in Wilmer, Texas. Daily jaunts through the countryside gave her a lifelong love of nature and the outdoors, and long nights spent reading afforded a great appreciation of the written word. She graduated from Southern Methodist University with degrees in English and geology and went on to obtain a doctorate degree in marine geology from the University of Southern California, where she served as chief scientist aboard their research ship R/V Velero IV under the guidance of Dr. Donn Gorsline. After that, Suzanne worked as an environmental geologist for several decades, cleaning up pollution on land and sea, and consulting on wetlands restoration projects in coastal southern California. She taught geology and oceanography at El Camino College in Torrance, California for many years and has previously published a college-level laboratory manual for oceanography. Suzanne currently teaches Earth Science at Mount San Antonio College and resides on the edge of the Bolsa Chica wetlands of southern California with her daughters, Hannah and Norah.

Much of the material in this book also stems from the experiences of Suzanne's husband, Azzam Alwash. Born in 1958 in Kut, Iraq, he spent his youth in the town of Nasriya on the edge of the Mesopotamian Marshlands. His father, Jawad Alwash, took him on trips through the wetlands on many occasions, fostering in him a love for its natural beauty and respect for its human culture. Azzam attended Basra University and then immigrated to the United States, where he earned a degree in civil engineering from California State University at Fullerton and a doctorate in geotechnical engineering from the University of Southern California. He and Suzanne met in college and married in 1986. Azzam worked as a consulting geotechnical engineer for many years, designing grading plans and foundations. During the 1990s, he became active in Iraqi opposition politics, serving on the Board of Directors of the Iraqi Forum for Democracy and the Free Iraq Foundation and as a member of the expatriate Iraqi National Congress.

In 2001, Azzam and Suzanne founded the Eden Again Project to promote the restoration of the Mesopotamian Marshlands. The project began as a forlorn hope in the corner of their suburban home, but as they reached out to like-minded colleagues the movement gained support. The advent of war in brought an explosion of interest in the fabled marshes and the Eden Again Project moved from theory to practice. In 2003, Azzam resigned from his consulting practice and relocated to Iraq to begin work on the ground while Suzanne provided support for the project from California. In 2004 Azzam founded Iraq's first environmental organization, Nature Iraq, with Suzanne serving as its Senior Technical Advisor. In 2006, she brought their daughters to live in neighboring Jordan so that she could begin working directly in Iraq. Since then, Suzanne has traveled several times to the marshlands as a Senior Technical Advisor to the Nature Iraq team.

Nature Iraq has been designated as a national focal point for the Ramsar Convention on Wetlands; accredited by the United Nations Environmental Program; and is in the process of becoming BirdLife International's designated country partner. Azzam resigned from its daily operations in 2012 but continues to preside over its board of trustees. Now in its eighth year with a staff of 37 men and women, Nature Iraq continues to work throughout Iraq to address its diverse environmental issues. Although they have suffered through bombings, torture, and kidnapping, these heroes strive to look beyond the chaos of today towards that quixotic future where Iraqis can live in harmony both with each other and their environment.

from right to left, Suzanne Alwash, Azzam Alwash, and Abbas Dakhel in the dried Hammar Marsh, 2008.

≋ INTRODUCTION

The marshlands of southern Iraq represent a rare watery landscape in the midst of one of the world's largest desert regions. Its shallow lagoons harbor vast populations of endemic and migratory birds and its reedy mudflats sustain an abundant community of water-dependent wildlife. These wetlands shelter a valuable reservoir of our global biodiversity: the World Wildlife Fund has listed the area as one of the 200 most significant ecosystems in the world, deserving urgent conservation efforts.

These marshlands also carry universally-significant historical and cultural value. The rich resources of the ecosystem nourished the growth of the ancient Sumerian civilization and its current inhabitants carry on their millennia-old traditions. The world's first epic poem, Gilgamesh, was written on the marshland's watery shores , and religious scholars have proposed the marshlands as the Garden of Eden and the birthplace of the patriarch Abraham.

This book is intended to provide a broad overview of the history of the marshlands, the current status of its ecosystem and the precarious future of this invaluable asset. It focuses on the ecosystem—including the symbiotic relationship between the marsh dwellers and their natural environment—but details of the social customs of the marsh dweller culture are beyond the scope of this book. The information is intended for a general audience, although specialized researchers will appreciate the work for its breadth of coverage. Therefore the information is presented in an informal rather than a scholarly format, blending together historical narrative, nature writing, popular science, and personal memoir without extensive footnotes and citations. An extensive annotated bibliography has been provided at the end of this book for those who desire further details and sources. A list of abbreviations and acronyms (regrettably unavoidable in scientific and international development work) is also provided, along with a glossary of Arabic words (many of which have no English translation) used in the text.

The book begins with a description of the marshlands in the middle of the 20th century, drawing upon the descriptions of Wilfred Thesiger and others. The book continues with a description of the drying of the marshlands during the latter part of the century and then takes a step back, examining historical cycles of drying and rehydration of the wetlands as humans have attempted to control the ecosystem since the dawn of civilization. The next few chapters chronologically detail efforts to restore the marshlands after the fall of Saddam Hussein.

Subsequently, the book follows a more topical format, providing more detailed descriptions of the recovery of bird populations, the resurgence of the fishing industry, critical water resource issues, national legislation for marshland protection, international efforts to conserve the marshlands, and the socioeconomic recovery of the marsh dwellers.

The penultimate chapter describes the suffering in the marshlands during the water shortages of 2008-2009 and efforts to halt their desiccation. Finally, the book ends with a discussion of the steps that must be taken to preserve this precious resource.

Scattered throughout this work are the stories of the people who have worked to save the marshes. Most of these people had been just as devastated by the former Iraqi regime as the marshes had been. In some ways, the act of restoring the environment has somehow purged them of their old injuries; as they healed the marshlands, they too have been made whole again.

1. THE MA'DAN AND THEIR MARSHES

"Memories of that first visit to the Marshes have never left me: firelight on a half-turned face, the crying of geese, duck flighting in to feed, a boy's voice singing somewhere in the dark, canoes moving in procession down a water-way, the setting sun seen crimson through the smoke of burning reed beds, narrow water-ways that wound still deeper into the Marshes. A naked man in a canoe with a trident in his hand, reed houses built upon water, black, dripping buffaloes that looked as if they had calved from the swamp with the first dry land. Stars reflected in dark water, the croaking of frogs, canoes coming home at evening, peace and continuity, the stillness of a world that never knew an engine. Once again I experienced the longing to share this life, and to be more than a mere spectator."

—Wilfred Thesiger, *The Marsh Arabs*

The Mesopotamian Marshlands, a vast expanse of towering emerald reeds studded with placid azure pools, lie within one of the most unrelentingly arid regions of the world. Surrounded by sere desert plains, these wetlands owe their existence not to local precipitation but to the enormous flows of the Tigris and Euphrates Rivers. Indeed, all life in Mesopotamia—literally, the "land between the rivers"—depends upon them for sustenance.

The headwaters of these mighty streams originate far away in the Taurus and Zagros mountain ranges of modern Turkey, Iraq and Iran. There, they course as swift mountain streams cascading tumultuously through steep gorges until they reach the plateaus of northern Syria and Iraq, where they cut deep courses in the relatively soft bedrock. In this section they flow tranquilly, descending gradually to a few hundred feet above sea level as they enter the alluvial valley, still hundreds of miles from the ocean. In that vast Mesopotamian Plain, the once-swift mountain rivers snake their way sluggishly as lazy, braided streams.

From the head of the plain to the Gulf[1], the rivers meander slowly. The loss of velocity and turbulence causes the rivers to deposit their silt, thereby building up their beds and banks above the level of the plain, a characteristic that makes them prone to overflow their banks seasonally and to change course capriciously. About 100 miles (160 km) south of Baghdad, the slope decreases even further, with elevations dropping only about one foot per mile (0.2 m/km). With little pressure to flow seaward, the Tigris and the Euphrates begin to split like the branches of a tree, forming vast inland deltas. The levees gradually become lower and broader, groundwater rises to the surface, and shallow depressions between the channels become marshy. Eventually the channels disappear altogether and the maze of the marshlands begins.

After passing through the marshes, the twin rivers regain their identity near the city of Qurna, where they join to form the river known as Shatt al-Arab. Just after passing Basra, another great river—the Karun—joins the flow of the Shatt al-Arab. Nearing the Gulf, their combined water becomes increasingly saline until finally the river once again disintegrates into the labyrinth channels of the Shatt al-Arab tidal estuary.

The Mesopotamian Marshes can be divided into three broad units defined by the tenuous boundaries of these rivers: the Central Marshes between the Tigris and Euphrates Rivers; the Hawizeh Marshes east of the Tigris River; and the Hammar Marshes south of the Euphrates River. This vast ecosystem, historically covering around 5,000 square miles[2] (13,000 km^2), somewhat larger than the Florida Everglades, represents an ever-changing mosaic of permanent and seasonal marshes, shallow and deep-water lakes, mudflats, flowing rivers, and seasonally inundated desert. The highly gradational environment gives rise to an array of diverse habitats and environmental conditions that are intricately interconnected and stand in high contrast to the surrounding desert.

In addition to the permanent marshlands, a variety of ephemeral wetlands historically developed along the fringes of the continuously-inundated areas. Springtime flooding over the banks of the Tigris River

---

[1] The body of water that separates the Arabian Peninsula and Iran is usually referred to by cartographers as the Persian Gulf, but most Iraqis refer to the bay as the Arabian Gulf. We have elected to refer to this body of water as simply "the Gulf."

[2] Estimates of the size of the wetlands vary widely based upon which wetland units are considered to "belong" within the Mesopotamian Marshland group and whether or not seasonal wetlands are included, and which time period is being cited as the standard. In this book, estimates include the Central, Hawizeh, and Hammar permanent and seasonal marshes, and the seasonal marshes along the Tigris River up to Kut, based upon satellite images from the 1970s.

Figure 1. Regional Location

and the Shatt al-Arab created vast seasonal marshlands, most notably the Saadiya and Sanniya marshes that historically sheltered enormous flocks of migratory waterfowl. In the desert south of Hammar Marsh, depressions known as *sebkha* would temporarily fill with water and then evaporate, leaving behind a carpet of cavernous mud cracks filled with crystalline salt. Saline wetlands also appeared north of Hawizeh Marsh, sustaining flocks of pink flamingoes adapted to feasting on the brine shrimp that thrive in those salty waters. And in the foothills of the Zagros Mountains rising to the east of the marshes, artesian springs bubbled up along the toes of alluvial fans, creating jewel-like oases in the surrounding desert.

THE MID-CENTURY MARSHES

The outside world gains much of its knowledge of these Mesopotamian Marshlands from the writings of British explorer Wilfred Thesiger. In 1951, weary from spending years in the dusty sands of the Arabian Desert, he ventured northward to explore the fabled wetlands of Iraq. The intrepid traveler ventured into the belly of the marshes with an eager anticipation, not knowing that they would become his home for much of the next seven years.

Thesiger fell in love. The marshes drew him back again and again, and to support his leisurely trips through the reeds, he wrote *The Marsh Arabs* (published in 1964). His descriptions of the marshes and the unique culture that they have spawned continue to be appreciated for his sensitive portrayal of an indigenous people and their symbiotic relationship with the surrounding ecosystem. The remainder of this chapter relies heavily upon his work and words.

Thesiger spent most of his time in the area known as the Central Marshes, bounded on the east by the Tigris, on the south by the Euphrates, and to the west by a labyrinth string of freshwater lagoons representing the remnant of a former course of the Tigris. The permanent marshes covered around 1,000 square miles (2,600 km^2), expanding to 1,500 (3,900 km^2) with the development of a seasonal wetland fringe following floods. The Central Marshes are watered from the north by distributary branches of the Tigris after it passes through the great rice-growing region of the inland delta, and also from the south by floods overtopping the left-bank levees of the Euphrates.

Entering the area from the north, Thesiger ventured into the

Figure 2. The Marshlands Area

vegetation-choked marshes, traveling along narrow channels that wound through a seemingly impenetrable palisade of reeds (dominantly *Australis phragmites)* growing up to twenty feet (6 m) high. Like thick stalks of bamboo, the stems of the older reeds could reach several inches (7 cm) in circumference, sporting at their tops tawny inflorescences that waved like pennants above the green stalks. In some areas, giant cane grass stretched up even higher than the reeds, while small stands of papyrus fluttered their airy tufts between those giant thickets. Cattails or reedmace *(Typha angustifolia)* lined the channel banks, their slender emerald stalks mirrored in the unruffled water, and sedges or rushes sprouted quickly in temporarily flooded areas.

Occasionally the reed beds would open up onto small, enclosed ponds where cool breezes blew over still pools of viscous water. Thesiger explored the intimate waters of Birkat Baghdadiya, scarcely a mile (1.6 km) across, and the elongate Hawr Zichri, snaking about seven miles (11 km) through the marsh. Each pond had its own character: those with more alkalinity had clear water overlying barren, pearly grey mud; others had highly fertile waters the color of pea soup covering peaty brown sediments that reeked with hydrogen sulfide. In other areas, tiny specks of lime-green duckweed or the heavy mats of glaucous water soldier carpeted the water's surface, giving it the appearance of a grassy meadow.

As he drifted through these ancient lagoons, Thesiger encountered watery villages built upon groups of man-made islands nestled within the reeds. Each island housed one extended family and their livestock within simple homes built of reeds. While remote settlements may have had only a few islands, the more populous "towns" could contain hundreds. During his sojourns, Thesiger probably visited every village in the Central Marshes, but his favorites were the settlements known as Saigal, Qabiba, and Bu Mughaifat, where he became as welcome as one of their own tribe.

He learned that the islands, barely edging above the surface of the water, had been built up over the centuries by intercalations of reeds and mud, as the family added a new layer each year to replace the elevation lost through decomposition. The structures atop the islands, constructed from bundles of reeds formed into arches and covered with layers of reed mats, measured about eight by twenty feet (2.5 by 6 m). The family inhabited one side while livestock enjoyed the other (typically more spacious) end.

Outside on the open platform, water buffalo (Domestic or Asian Water Buffalo, *Bubalus bubalis*) would loll on the spongy reeds while barking dogs warned off intruders. Smoke rolled from outdoor kitchens where women prepared the daily meal, their exquisitely gaudy dresses of vermillion, electric blue or iridescent green providing flashes of color in the monotonous green and brown environment. Their babies crawled freely across the compound, kept from falling off the island by reed fences opening up to the family wharf, where a row of slender canoes could be found.

Towering over each village was at least one *mudhif*, a veritable palace of reeds ostensibly owned by one of the local leaders but that in reality served the whole village as its town council, community center, and hostel for weary visitors. The typical building measured 13 feet wide, 16 feet tall, and 60 feet long (4 m wide, 5 m tall, and 18 m long), although the grandest examples could span 120 feet (36 m). Its main structural elements were its arches. Each arch was constructed by setting two long, tightly bound bundles of reeds into the ground opposite each other, the width of the house apart and sloping outward. The tops of the bundles were then pulled inward and spliced one into the other to form a horseshoe arch. Next, workmen fastened transverse bundles of reeds and then affixed overlapping reed mats onto this framework. The "cornerstones" of the building were formed of reed pillars measuring a few feet (1 m) in diameter at their base and tapering upwards to a point above the roofline. Alternating squares of reed trellis and matting decorated the end panels of the *mudhif*, while open trellis work adorned its lower walls to allow influx of cool breezes.

Inside, the earthen floors were covered with more reed matting strewn with woven rugs and arrayed with cushions along the walls. A strip of bare earth in the center of the *mudhif* housed the hearth where a row of brass coffeepots with long, curving beaks simmered over a fire of dried reeds. A strict code of conduct governed relations inside the *mudhif*, based upon the principles of Bedouin hospitality and honor. This was a males-only realm; boys could enter to serve coffee and entertain, while covered women were only allowed entrance if they came bearing huge trays of food for the communal table.

The waterways between the islands of the village teemed with craft of all kinds, flashing black against the sparkling water. The majority were slim canoes with upturned prows called *mashuf*, the workhorse of the marshes. The flat-bottomed vessel, built of bitumen-covered planks, has both curved bow and stern for parting the thick curtains of reeds. The marsh men preferred to pole these canoes and would only kneel and paddle when the water was too deep for poling; they could easily travel 50 miles (80 km) in a day in this manner. Children played in smaller canoes called *chalabiya* or fashioned rafts out of bundles of cut reeds. Larger, sturdier boats, called *balam*, transported passengers and marsh products to the larger market towns and brought back staples such as sugar, tea, rice, flour, henna and tobacco.

But it was the war canoe known as *tarada* that was truly a breathtaking masterpiece of watercraft. This craft, reminiscent of Viking vessels, typically measured 36 feet (11 m) long and 3 feet (1 m) wide, its front sweeping forward and upward in a long, menacing claw. The *tarada* was normally reserved for the greatest of tribal leaders, yet one of the local elders, Sheikh Falih, presented Thesiger with a superb example for his own personal use.

When Thesiger floated his magnificent *tarada* off into the marshlands, four young boatmen eagerly joined him; while all four eventually became like his brothers, the naturally aristocratic Amara, haughty and fine-boned as an Arabian stallion, always remained his favorite. The men drifted into the green womb of the wetlands, paddling through the watery forest past thickets of willow and tamarisk lining the riparian banks. Every evening, the amiable companions would moor their *tarada* at a reed island where the host, a complete stranger, would welcome them hospitably, feeding, entertaining and housing them for the night.

A keen observer of human nature and laden with a naturally intense curiosity, Thesiger slowly grew to understand these people who called themselves "Marsh Arabs." The society seemed to be segmented into classes based upon occupation rather than racial divides. Estimates of the population of Marsh Arabs at the time vary widely as there was no formal census, but range between 300,000 to 500,000. The majority of these were actually farmers, or *fellah*, who lived on the upstream fringes of the marsh and were only partially dependent on its natural resources for their subsistence. Although they husbanded a few water buffalo for the benefit of their own household and went to the marshes to cut fodder for the livestock, to fish and to hunt birds for their own consumption, their primary economic activity was growing rice.

In contrast, the *ma'dan*[3] owed their entire existence to the bounty of the marshes, and their population at the time probably ranged from

---

[3] Although ma'dan is the traditional noun describing the people who live in the Iraqi marshes, it is also used as a pejorative term, and most ma'dan prefer to call themselves "Marsh Arabs." We have chosen to use the more general term "marsh dweller" to denote the population that is dependent on the marshes for their survival.

50,000 to 100,000. These true marsh dwellers subsisted through an elaborate exploitation of the reeds themselves, weaving their dry stems into mats and feeding their green shoots to water buffalo for the production of milk and dung, carrying on a daily routine inherited from a millennia-old tradition.

Every morning the reed cutters would head out from their villages in a cheerful flotilla of *mashuf* accompanied by herds of shaggy water buffalo swimming out for their daily forage and wallow. From a standing position in the boat, the workers would bend over and cut the reeds at the waterline using a small serrated arching blade, carefully selecting only the older, dried reeds for the finest mats. As they worked, the marsh would come alive as their chattering and singing added to the cacophony of birds and frogs. At midday, they returned to their village with each *mashuf* loaded with cut reeds stacked almost as high as the person standing to pole them.

After a simple lunch of grilled fish or duck alongside rice covered with yogurt and a handful of seasonal herbs, the entire family would participate in weaving the mats. First the canes were split lengthwise with a knife then pounded with a pestle to make them pliant, and finally woven diagonally into a four- by eight-foot (1.2 by 2.4 m) mat. Some women worked separately, specializing in weaving finer mats and baskets from the leaves of sedges and palm fronds. As enough mats were produced, traders collected the product and loaded them onto reed rafts or barges for transport to the city's markets.

Later in the afternoon, the *mashuf* would advance again to the marshes to gather fodder to sustain the water buffalo through the night. Now their efforts focused on cropping the youngest, greenest reed shoots known as *hashish*. As evening approached, the water buffalo would find their way home and heave themselves onto the family platform dripping like the keel of a boat, groaning in a voice of infinite despair, and the family would rush to care for them in privileged luxury.

Every family kept a few buffalo and felt a deep attachment to the ponderous beasts who shared their lives and homes. A marsh man could recognize not only his own buffalo's voice and silhouette from a great distance, but also those belonging to his neighbors and even the herds from distant villages. In turn, the buffalo knew its owner by both sight and smell, and would only allow that person to milk her. If circumstances forced the owner to temporarily leave his buffalo in someone else's charge, the caretaker must necessarily wear the owner's clothes, cover his face, and remain silent while approaching the animal.

Dairy products represented an important commercial export

from the marsh. Water buffalo milk has an extremely high fat content and sweet butter could be produced by churning it inside a sheepskin pouch. But a creamy cheese known as *ghaymer*, produced only in the marshes, was the true delicacy prized throughout Iraq. Each evening, the housewife would boil the milk and leave it to cool; in the morning the smoky, silken *ghaymer* would be skimmed off for breakfast. The remaining buttermilk would either be drank with meals or made into yogurt to serve over rice.

Buffalo also produced copious amounts of dung. In a world without wood, this by-product seemed at times more vital than the dairy, and the buffalo simply machines used to process reed into fuel. Invariably it was the girls who collected the fresh steaming offal and formed it into patties incorporating bits of chopped reed, leaving behind an imprint of their hand as they slapped the fuel cake onto the side of a reed fence for drying.

The buffalo were so valuable that some tribes specialized in herding them, and a single buffalo-herding family could own anywhere from 20 to 200 beasts. The lifestyle of the buffalo herders was necessarily more nomadic as the people followed their herds in search of fresh pasturage, and their culture as a result subtly different, more makeshift than the marsh dwellers of the villages. When summer's heat and mosquitoes threatened the livestock's health, the tribe would deconstruct their reed huts and load their entire household possessions—consisting mostly of reed mats, a few blankets, fishing spears, cooking pots and utensils— onto their *mashuf* and establish temporary villages alongside rivers and canals, where the cooling breeze made life more bearable.

During his travels, Thesiger always brought along medical supplies to help treat the rampant illnesses he encountered. Doctors never ventured into the marshes, and the marsh dwellers harbored intense suspicion of the hospitals in the city and therefore suffered greatly from untreated injuries and infectious disease. The rate of infant mortality was appallingly high. Nearly everyone was infected with bilharzia (a parasite carried by snails and causing the disease Schistosomiasis), but Thesiger found surprisingly little malaria; he speculated that the endemic mosquitoes were probably a poor carrier of the parasite. The population also suffered from trachoma, intestinal worms of several varieties, and periodic epidemics of measles, chickenpox, mumps, whooping cough, and influenza. Dysentery was rife as the marsh dwellers used the same waterways for water supply and waste disposal. In addition to treating illness, Thesiger also became famous in the marshes for his skill in circumcision, and apparently performed thousands of these operations during his sojourn.

THE HAWIZEH MARSHES

Nomadic in nature, Thesiger sometimes grew tired of the intimate terrain of the domesticated Central Marshes and occasionally longed for the untamable wilderness of the Hawizeh Marshes east of the Tigris River. Straddling the Iran-Iraq border, these shadowy wetlands were known to be rife with smugglers and brigands who discouraged the development of permanent settlements, so Thesiger insisted that his trusted boatmen from the Central Marshes accompany him as he crossed the Tigris into the vast unknown territory.

The Hawizeh marshes are fed from the Iraqi side by two channels of the Tigris, the Kahla and the Musharra, which depart from it around Amara; water also spills directly over the left-bank levees of the Tigris when it floods. From the Iranian side, the Karkheh River nourishes its own significant wetland known there as the Azim Marsh. At that time, Hawizeh covered about a thousand square miles of wetlands and affiliated habitats that were ecologically very similar to those to the west except for the presence of several large, deeper lakes including Umm al-Niaj and Umm al-Binni[4].

Winter storms on these lakes churned up waves high enough to overturn even Thesiger's sturdy *tarada*; people regularly drowned in their depths, and his boatmen refused to cross over the open water, paddling around their edges instead. The wind and waves would tear off huge chunks of the reed beds on the lake's periphery, pulling the plants up by their roots and creating natural reed rafts spanning thirty feet (9 m) across that drifted like icebergs across the lakes. These drifting sheets of vegetation, called *tehela*, were hardly distinguishable from their *in situ* habitat, and their constant rearrangement on the lake obliterated landmarks and made navigation in the sparsely-inhabited territory even more difficult.

The lakes were filled with ten to twenty feet (3 to 6 m) of exceptionally clear water harboring a rich mosaic of submerged aquatic plants. Gazing into their depths, Thesiger could see feathery branches of chartreuse hornwort and water milfoil stretching to the surface next to dancing stands of holly-leafed water nymph. White water lilies floated above leathery strands of olive-green eel grass undulating in underwater meadows, while wispy sago pondweed and small leaves of

---

[4] Umm al-Binni Lake has been postulated to represent a meteor impact crater dating from around 5,000 years ago.

floating water fern clung to the canoe boys' paddles.

But mostly there were reed beds, and these trembled with hidden wildlife. Snakes, some innocuous and others poisonous, slithered between the damp roots, while Euphrates Soft-shell Turtles *(Rafetus euphraticus)* splashed off the mucky banks. Rodents furtively scuttled between the reeds—mostly ordinary field mice, rats, hedgehogs, and shrews—along with others known only in the marshes, such as the Mesopotamian or Harrison's Gerbil *(Gerbillus mesopotamiae)*, a species uniquely dependent on this wetland habitat for its survival. More rarely Thesiger would encounter larger mammals, such as hyenas, jackals, mongoose, and the ferocious Honey Badger *(Mellivora capensis)* that would kill and eat almost anything. Grey Wolves *(Canis lupus)* roamed the periphery of the marshes, searching hungrily for the dwindling herds of liquid-eyed Goitered Gazelle *(Gazella subgutturosa)* that grazed in the meadows of the seasonal marshes.

Old men told tales of lions and leopards stalking the marshlands, but the last known marshland lion was shot in 1945. The only feline remaining at that time in the marshlands was the Jungle Cat *(Felis chaus)*. Lynx-like, with pointed ears, long legs and a slender build, the cat usually has a faintly striped, sandy to reddish-brown coat. They feed in the daytime on rodents, frogs, and birds, but will also dive to catch fish, returning to the reed thickets to sleep within small hollows lined with old cane leaves and fur.

But by far the largest and most prominent mammals of the marshes were the Wild Boars *(Sus scrofa)*, standing up to four feet (1.2 m) tall, relentlessly persecuted because of the danger they posed. The huge beasts would attack anyone and everything, charging out of the reeds without warning. Most marsh men travelled with a weapon, usually a gun dating from World War I, to defend themselves against the shaggy beasts. Thesiger had repaired many people who had been gored by their razor-sharp tusks, and he enthusiastically joined in the attempt to exterminate the scourge, shooting almost 500 over a two-year period.

In 1956, Thesiger brought the Scotsman Gavin Maxwell to Hawizeh, and Maxwell's heart was stolen by the wildlife of this deep wilderness. He watched delightedly as boisterous otters darted in and out of the waters; both the Common Otter *(Lutra lutra)* and the Smooth-coated Otter *(Lutra perspicillata)* occur in these waters. Noting his enthusiasm, Thesiger presented him with a newly-weaned pup and Maxwell brought it back with him to England as a pet. Zoologists at the British Museum of Natural History declared it a creature hitherto unknown to science, and designated the subspecies as Maxwell's Smooth-coated

Otter *(Lutra perspicillata maxwellii)*. Ensconced in his London flat, the rascally dervish caused Maxwell no end of trouble, and in desperation they moved to a remote island near the Isle of Skye, where the otter frolicked in the local marsh and Maxwell entered into what he termed "a thralldom to otters." Maxwell's account of his experiences with the irrepressible creature, *Ring of Bright Water*, became a best-selling book and film, and the island where they lived is now an otter sanctuary.

CHUBAYISH AND THE HAMMAR MARSHES

Thesiger occasionally visited the larger marshland towns situated on the northern bank of the Euphrates River between the Central and Hammar marshes. The largest of these, Chubayish, boasted a population of 30,000 people living on a dense network of 1,600 islands. The city, dubbed "the Venice of Iraq," was famous for its natural beauty: the narrow canals separating the islands were lined with over 15,000 date palms, while fruit trees drooped heavy with oranges over the water. Footbridges made from the trunks of palm trees connected many of the islands, although every family owned several *mashuf*, which were the primary means of transport. The city had one paved street where the government offices, shops, school and clinic could be found— but as the village was surrounded entirely by water, this single street connected with no other road.

South of Chubayish lay the vast expanse of the Hammar Marshes, which extended from Nasriya in the west to the outskirts of Basra on the Shatt al-Arab in the east. This marsh area covered about 1,000 square miles (2,600 km^2) of permanent wetlands and lakes, expanding to nearly 1,500 square miles (3,900 km^2) during periods of seasonal and temporary inundation. Hammar was fed primarily by right-bank flooding and tributaries of the Euphrates, although a considerable amount of water also overflowed from the Central Marshes and bubbled up from underground.

The dominant feature of this area was the great sweep of Hammar Lake, a wide expanse of sunny open water measuring about 75 miles (120 km) long. Standing on its shores, one could see water extending as far as the eye could see, as lake and sky blended into one across an invisible horizon. White caps could develop during high winds, and the lake was considered extremely treacherous by the marsh dwellers. The water, ranging from five to ten feet (1.5 to 3 m) deep, was slightly brackish due to its connection with the ocean and subject to the influence of tides. Permanent marshes surrounded the lake, but during the summer large parts of the lake would dry out and banks and islands emerged.

Like most of the smaller ponds across the marshlands, Hammar Lake supported an abundant fishery, and numerous groups of fishermen lived seasonally along its shores, building makeshift conical huts of reeds as temporary homes. The estimated catch of fish in the marshes during this time was 33,000 tons (30,000 tonnes) annually. The lake and its surrounding marshes provided an important habitat for an unusually rich fish fauna resulting from the mingling of fish derived from western or Syrian sources (via the Euphrates), eastern or Zagrosian sources (via the Tigris and its tributaries), and marine sources (via the Shatt al-Arab). Various species of freshwater cyprinids dominated the fish population, although several anadromous fish species of great economic importance, such as the pomphret and shad, also depended on the estuarine ecosystem for spawning. Even the tiny penaeid shrimp undertook seasonal migrations between its spawning grounds in the Gulf and its nursery in the marshes.

Marsh dwellers traditionally speared their prey with a five-pronged trident while standing astride the bow of a *mashuf.* Their favorite catch was the *gattan* (*Luciobarbus xanthopterus*, formerly known as *Barbus xanthopterus*), a fatty fish weighing up to 30 pounds (14 kg). Moonless nights could find an entire phalanx of *mashuf* lined up on the lake, reed torches hanging from each prow behind which stood a man wielding a ten-foot-long (3 m) trident seeking his succulent prey.

Another common method of night fishing was the *hauwa*, used for catching large amounts of small fish called *zurri.* Two canoes would pull next to each other with lanterns hanging from the outboard sides. As the boatmen poled along, tiny silver flashes literally jumped into the boats, to be taken home, fried crispy and eaten whole.

Spearing individual fish was a labor-intensive job, and some marsh men achieved greater success through the use of natural toxins. They collected the poisonous fruit of local jimson weeds, processed the product and placed it within bait that was scattered in a lake; the stunned fish could be collected by hand a few hours later. The marsh dwellers historically used these biodegradable poisons selectively, only to capture specific large fish while leaving the remainder unharmed. But during the 1970s, synthetic poisons were made available in Iraq, and unscrupulous fishermen would spread them across the surface of the lake, killing all of its fish. The effect of the persistent poison intensified as it moved up the food chain, and populations of the larger resident fish-eating birds began to decrease.

In Thesiger's day, only the tribe known as *Berbera* (their relationship, if any, to the Berbers of northern Africa is unclear) used nets to capture fish. But the introduction of motor boats into the marshes during the 1960s allowed for the rapid transport of the daily catch to the markets of Basra and Baghdad, and netting fish became commonplace in the resultant boom. Groups of marsh men would cast out billowing nets in small ponds, or set out gill nets across narrow channels to capture fish with the ebbing tide; even drift nets could be found bobbing along in the smaller rivers on floaters made from palm frond stalks.

The most unique type of fishing developed in the marshes was inspired by a method used by pelicans to capture their prey. In the *hillawi* technique, a 500-foot-long (150 m) roll of coarsely-woven fabric was extended in a semi-circle across the lake; men wading in the waist-high water herded fish into the open end while the net was slowly closed. Then the bottom edge of the net was fixed to the ground, and men inside this cheesecloth corral would shuffle their feet in the lake bed sediments to make the water turbid. The fish, their gills choked with clay, would rise to the surface gasping for air where they would be caught by hand.

SEASONS IN THE MARSHES

Thesiger was drawn back to the marshes time and again, its annual rhythm of birth, death, and rebirth resonating deep within him. Springtime in the marshes was a short pastel glory, when the lengthening days turned the marshlands into a balmy green meadow of *hashish* dotted with yellow and white water buttercups. An explosion of frogs transformed the marshes' peace into a babel of croaks, creeks, burps, bellows, and ribbits. But then the blustery *Sharqi* wind would blow in from the east-southeast, and violent thunderstorms with splintery lightning would travel down the plain, vividly reminding him why weather was a god in ancient times.

In March, the snowpack of the Taurus and Zagros mountains would begin to melt, releasing vast quantities of water. During these floods, the rivers could carry torrents ten times as great as during the low flow period of late summer. Villages would be inundated with floods that lifted the layers of reeds off their foundations, causing the islands to hover above their foundations. The imperturbable marsh dwellers would simply hang their valuables, including small infants, from the rafters of their huts and continue with their daily lives.

The flood pulse served as a major driving force in the ecology of the marshlands. Flooding cooled, freshened, and deepened the water in the permanent marsh and lakes, flushing out salt and algae and triggering key botanical responses. The floodwaters expanded the area of the wetlands, creating mudflats around the permanent marshes where nutrients were recycled and tiny worms, clams, shrimps and snails thrived and fattened in the organic slime. As the floods abated, small rice paddies could be planted on the banks of rivers and canals and on the borders of the marshes. The late spring and early summer would witness an enormous rate of vegetal growth; during this time, the daily growth of reeds could be visually discerned.

The verdant wetlands sheltered an enormous variety of breeding birds that sometimes coalesced in huge multi-species nesting colonies containing up to 10,000 herons, cranes, ducks, waders, and warblers. The marshlands were important breeding grounds for several endangered species, including a substantial proportion of the world's population of the rare Marbled Duck *(Marmaronetta angustirostris)* and the entire world population of the Middle Eastern subspecies of the snake-necked African Darter *(Anhinga rufa chantrei)*, along with isolated populations of two other primarily Afro-tropical species: the Goliath Heron *(Ardea goliath)*, nearly as large as a man, and the Sacred Ibis *(Threskiornis aethiopicus)*, long venerated in the Middle East. For two endemic species, the Iraq Babbler *(Turdoides altirostris)* and the Basra Reed Warbler *(Acrocephalus griseldis)*, the marshes served as their only known breeding ground.

In August, temperatures generally peaked over 110°F (43°C) with heat waves reaching up to 130°F (54°C). The wetlands become a mosquito-infested sauna and marsh dwellers would build elevated sleeping platforms to catch relief from the *Shamal*, a dry steady wind blowing down from the northwest desert. Virtually no rain fell between June and October and evaporation gradually increased the salinity of water, but again the brine triggered important life cycle changes in the flora and fauna of the wetlands. As the water dried, air reached the roots of the reeds and bulrushes, bringing vital oxygen. The seasonal marshes gradually dried, leaving meadows of sweet grass that drew nomadic sheep herders, the *shawiyya*, to their desiccated shores.

Autumn provided a brief respite from the heat, punctuated by violent dust storms driven in by the return of the *Sharqi* wind. Dates were harvested in September, and some marsh dwellers would pack up their entire household onto their *mashuf* and migrate out to the date-packing factories near Basra. During November, rice was harvested in the fields just upstream of the marshes, and again some locals migrated out to assist; in both cases, they were typically paid with a portion of the harvest, as the Marsh Arab culture despised those who worked for wages.

About six inches of rain drizzled down during the winter wet season. The rivers experienced a minor rise that spilled over into the parched soil of the marshes, freshening its lakes and channels. Winter days were usually glorious with clear indigo skies and cool temperatures, although winter nights could be bitterly cold, leaving trails of hoary frost decorating the damp ground. The landscape turned sepia, the tawny reeds rustling like paper as their soft creamy plumes dipped and danced in the breeze, and tufts of wheaten seed drifted down from the cinnabar fruit pods of the cattails. The air carried the dusky tang of distant smoke as buffalo herders set fires in the dried reed beds to encourage new growth of *hashish* in the spring.

During this period of senescence the avian diversity and population burgeoned as winter visitors arrived from their Siberian summering grounds—geese in long-winged flight, squadrons of bulky pelicans, and rafts of densely packed coots settled on the waters and mudflats of the marshes. The Mesopotamian Marshlands provided habitat for two-thirds of the wintering wildfowl of the Middle East: in 1979, a mission of the International Waterfowl and Wetlands Research Bureau, led by wildlife experts Eric Carp and Derek Scott, estimated that several million migratory waterfowl were sheltering in these marshlands. In addition to the birds that stayed all winter, the wetlands also represented an important rest stop for numerous species of herons, egrets, and shorebirds as they passed through on their migrations between Central Asia and Africa.

Fast behind the migratory waterfowl swooped the migratory birds of prey—eagles, harriers, kestrels, and hawks. Human hunters noticed the spiraling predators and eagerly followed their lead: wild birds were an important food source for the marsh dwellers. Fowlers used a specialized canoe, the *mataur*, which was about half the length of a *mashuf*, slightly broader and even closer to the waterline. This configuration allowed a man to lay belly-down while slowly paddling from downwind toward a flock of birds, yet the proficient fowler could also fire at ducks on the wing while standing on this precarious perch, sometimes only a little larger than a water-ski.

Winter months provided the best hunting, when a proficient marksman could bag 60 birds in one day, his only limit being the capacity of his boat to carry the take home. The flocks at this time were so vast that no one worried that they would have any impact on their population, as more birds came back year after year. The most desirable quarry were the fat, tasty water birds—teal, pochard, goose, gadwall, shoveller, and wigeon—but the marsh dwellers would eat almost any type of bird, even herons, cormorants, ibis, and flamingoes. The only ones that they would not consume, due to Islamic dietary restrictions, were the raptors or other meat-eating fowl such as crows and seagulls.

THE MARSHES IN THE 1970S

In 1952, Gavin Young was a shipping clerk in Basra when Thesiger invited him on one of his trips to the marshes. Like his mentor, Young felt a deep connection with this complex ecosystem and its indigenous culture, and he visited them frequently over the next few years. There followed a 17-year interregnum, until Young was lured by an overwhelming nostalgia to return to the marshes. Many people tried to dissuade him: things would be different, they said, the marsh dwellers would not remember him, his heart would be broken and his dreams shattered. Yet he returned, accompanied by the talented photographer Nik Wheeler, to document what he felt could be the waning days of this unique culture.

In a town on the edge of the marshes, Young was immediately recognized by a minor police official, who helped him rent a *balam*, now equipped with an outboard motor. The watery paradise that had previously never heard a motor now roared with their sound. His heart leapt in his throat as he passed the empty shoreline where once lived Sheikh Falih, now long dead, the first host of Thesiger and Young as they entered the marshes. Then he entered the village of Qabab, its shaggy reed houses scattered over a hundred islands looking exactly the same as he had remembered. Once again Young—seemingly a total stranger—was welcomed into the *mudhif* where he was greeted loudly and heartily by everyone. Then one man turned, and Young recognized the equine profile of Amara, Thesiger's boatman and brother, and he knew he had returned home.

As he spoke with the men in the *mudhif*, Young learned that during the late 1950s, after the oilfields of Basra began production and well-paying jobs were apparently plentiful, a wave of migration took place from the countryside into the towns. Tales of huge daily pay lured the rural inhabitants to the city, until they found that prices for food and lodging soon ate up their earnings, leaving them poorer than they had been in the country. But Young happily discovered that the migration had mostly involved *fellah* farming on the edges of the marshes, and that the reed villages of *ma'dan* within the marshes were still largely intact.

New economic opportunities had opened up in the marshes, including a sugar plantation and a factory that manufactured paper from reeds. The introduction of motor boats had greatly increased the village's access to markets, enabling them to sell their products on a more regular basis. Although most people still engaged in the traditional activities of reed-weaving, fishing, and buffalo herding, to Young the villagers seemed more prosperous than before.

Education had arrived in Qabab: all of the village boys attended classes in the reed schoolhouse, paddling themselves to school in their small *chalabiya*. The teacher, on a nine-month stint from Baghdad, wore a neat business suit as he taught the basics of reading, writing, and English while keeping his balance on the spongy reed platform. Mosquitoes permitting, classes were held outdoors under the balmy bowl of blue sky. Schoolboys competed fiercely in afternoon volleyball games.

Now medical care also reached the village: a doctor treated patients in his rustic dispensary and also visited nearby villages several times a week in a mobile clinic housed within a specially-designed *balam*. Malnutrition appeared to be a thing of the past, although bilharzia still stubbornly resisted elimination, along with tuberculosis, trachoma, dysentery, and bronchitis.

Young engaged some boatmen and an ancient marsh man as a guide, and his days began to take the shape of former times as he became reacquainted with the complex ecosystem, invigorated by the pulse of life around him. He was overjoyed to once again see abundant flocks of birds: to him, they were the marshes' crowning beauty. Young exulted in the flashing colors of the White-breasted Kingfisher *(Halcyon smyrnensis)* and the gaudy Purple Gallinule *(Porphyrio porphyrio)* as he drifted under a sky mottled with whirling concourses of geese.

He looked around at the new prosperity in the marshes: rudimentary schools, basic health care, and increased access to markets. At the time, it seemed to him that the marsh dwellers' way of life could last forever, as long as no "grand schemes" of the federal government interfered. He strongly approved of bringing modernity to the marshes rather than removing marsh dwellers to the cities.

"It would be a pity if [the Marsh Dwellers] were to abandon their ancestral homelands and become displaced peasants or factory-hands in anonymous overalls," he said in his memoir, *Return to the Marshes.* "It does not take long for proud rural peoples to go to seed in the amoral anarchy of towns. These marshes are alive. Real people live and work in them. They are not a variation on Disneyland."

2. DELIBERATE DEVASTATION

Revolution, chaos, and calamity will occur in the country. A dreadful (man), son of a nobody, whose name is not mentioned, will arise. As king he will seize the throne, he will destroy his lords with weapons. Half the troops of Akkad will fall in the gorges of Tupliash [an ancient city between southern Iraq and modern Iran]. *They will fill plain and hills. The people of the land will experience great scarcity ... the marshes and rivers will fill up with sand.*

—Akkadian Prophecies (ca. 1800 BC)

Gavin Young correctly predicted that the marshes would soon be threatened by "progressive" development schemes. Throughout the first half of the twentieth century, water control measures were implemented with the primary intention of reducing the occurrence of devastating floods and providing a better standard of living for farmers. In the 1960s, the government of Iraq envisaged a grand plan to fully develop the country's agricultural potential. An American engineering firm was hired to evaluate the available water resources of Iraq with the goal of harvesting almost all of its water for irrigation. But the study clearly stated that expansion of field agriculture would come at a cost: the desiccation of Iraq's downstream marshes. The engineers predicted that Iraq's proposed construction of dams and reservoirs would seriously deteriorate the economic and social well-being of the marsh dwellers dependent on fresh river water for drinking, rice cultivation, reed-based industries, and fishing. With thinly veiled discomfort, they concluded that full development of the extensive projects would entail "the marsh area ... inhabitants having to seek a new livelihood elsewhere."

Fortunately for the marshes, Iraq's plans to harvest all river water for field irrigation were never fully implemented. But then the 1970s ushered in an era of large dam construction in neighboring countries.

In 1973, Syria constructed the huge Tabqa Dam on the Euphrates, which was dwarfed by the Keban Dam constructed by Turkey in 1974 on the same river. Together, the dams could hold back an entire year's worth of the river's flow.

Notwithstanding the pressures from these dams, the marshes managed to maintain their integrity during the 1970s. The permanent areas of Hawizeh, Hammar, and the Central Marshes still covered around 4,000 square miles (10,000 km^2), but large swaths of the surrounding seasonal wetlands were beginning to disappear: these areas only received water during river flood stages, and the recently-constructed upstream reservoirs had greatly reduced the frequency and magnitude of floods.

Then another threat to the marshlands arose: petroleum development. Southern Iraq harbors around 5% of the world's total oil reserves. Seven giant oilfields (defined as having reserves exceeding one billion barrels) lie fully or partially beneath the historical marshlands, along with four supergiant oilfields holding estimated reserves totaling more than 70 billion barrels. Draining of the marshlands for oil extraction began in 1953; eventually 10% of the historical marsh area would be dried to accommodate petroleum production facilities.

THE IRAN-IRAQ WAR

Saddam Hussein al-Tikriti grew up as a fatherless boy from an unimportant family in a nondescript village north of Baghdad. As a young man, he joined the Ba'ath Party, where he distinguished himself by his charming personality, shrewd intellect, and enormous enthusiasm for torture. In 1968, the Ba'ath Party seized control of the Iraqi government and Saddam became an important behind-the-scenes player, organizing the secret police and overseeing prisons where political prisoners were interrogated and tortured. He gradually rose to prominence through a steady campaign of power consolidation and ruthless suppression of his enemies.

In 1979, Saddam declared himself President. A year later, Iraqi troops invaded Iran, and after brief but intense fighting, occupied a narrow strip of land along the shared border. For the first two years of the war, most of the fighting took place on Iranian soil; the Iranians ultimately regained their territory, however, and the next six years saw battles raging back and forth across the frontier.

The war was unpopular with the people of southern Iraq, many of whom felt close ties with their fellow Shi'a Muslims across the border. During the early 1980s, the regime began a program of ethnic cleansing, arresting Iraqi citizens with Iranian heritage under the claim that they were natural enemies of the state. Many of the detainees were from southern Iraq, where intermarriage with Iranians had been common. Men, women, and even children were incarcerated under inhumane conditions. Eventually Iraq deported 500,000 people to Iran, keeping only the males of military age, who were either conscripted into the army as disposable foot soldiers or executed.

Much of the Iran-Iraq war was fought over the sodden terrain of the southern marshlands. In 1984, Iran launched the infamous Battle of the Marshes. First, to clear the Iraqi minefields set along the battle lines, the Iranians sent out "human waves" consisting of thousands of Iranian foot soldiers. Ranging in age from only nine to more than fifty and driven by religious fervor, these soldiers died by the tens of thousands to clear safe paths for the regular army that followed.

The Iranians then surprised the Iraqi army by staging helicopter and water-borne attacks, utilizing small craft and rubber boats to penetrate the marshes. The swampy conditions helped the attackers to offset the defenders' advantage in tanks as they negotiated the marshes in boats and on foot along narrow strips of dry land.

The Iranians captured their initial objective, the Hawizeh oilfield known as the Majnoon Islands. But once they were past the marshes and in open country, they became easy targets of Iraq's well-entrenched forward positions. Iraq attacked with warplanes and helicopters, unleashing both conventional and chemical bombs, and the Iranians were pushed back. Estimates of the dead in this single battle vary from 25,000 to 50,000.

During the Iran-Iraq war, every young Iraqi man was required to serve at least two years in the army, but as the unpopular conflict dragged on, some chose to escape their military service. Many of these deserters moved into the marshes where they formed paramilitary cells. These resistance fighters plagued the government forces from the rear, and their numbers and successes gradually increased. But when troops stormed into the marshes in hot pursuit of the rebels, the fighters quickly disappeared, leaving the innocent marsh dwellers to bear the brunt of the army's wrath. Accused of providing material support to the resistance, many men of the marshes were arrested and their reed villages subsequently burned to ashes.

In 1985, Iran launched another attack, the Badr Offensive, through the Hawizeh marshes. Aggressively patrolling in small speedboats through the narrow waterways flanked by tall reeds, they flushed the Iraqis out of the marshes and pushed them back to fixed positions on dry land. Afterwards, both sides claimed control of Hawizeh and both utilized it for military purposes. For the next three years, the marshes would see frequent battles as each side tried to expel the other.

POST-WAR RETRIBUTION

The war concluded in 1988 with the political map of Iraq unchanged but its natural and human resources wholly ravaged. During the war, huge portions of southern Hawizeh had been alternately dried and flooded, as the combatants intended to either cross with its troops or repel enemy soldiers. An extensive series of causeways and dykes now crisscrossed the marshes, impeding the natural flow of water and inhibiting development of the seasonal marsh that would normally fringe the permanent wetland each spring. A dyke had been constructed across the southern and western borders of Hawizeh Marsh. A long causeway had been built from north to south across the Central Marshes to allow rapid troop transport, but its effect was to dry out the eastern third of the extensive wetlands. Yet 80% of the original permanent marshlands remained, providing a haven for the fighters who refused to lay down their weapons and continued to resist the Ba'ath government.

A 1989 memorandum prepared by a senior Iraqi security officer notes that despite large-scale operations against deserters and hostile elements in the marshes, the resistance fighters still engaged in subversive activities, using the marsh area as a launching pad for their operations. The memorandum calmly proposed a "Plan of Action for the Marshes," which included economic blockades, poisoning, explosions, burning of houses, assassinations, heavy artillery from helicopter gunships, and relocating marsh villages to dry land where the people could be more easily controlled. It was a blueprint for destroying the marsh dweller culture.

Thus the Iraqi government initiated a systematic depopulation of the marshes. In 1989 the army arrived at villages in the northern Central Marshes, including Saigal and Qabab, home to the beloved friends of Wilfred Thesiger. Gavin Young had revisited these villages in 1976 and found a thriving traditional culture buoyed with a new prosperity; the government had even built rudimentary clinics and reed schoolhouses and appointed doctors and teachers to care for the villagers. But now the troops stormed in on dozens of pontoon boats equipped with heavy weaponry while helicopter gunships circled overhead. The army forced the villagers onto the waiting boats and took them to nearby dry-land towns, warning them not to return to the marshes. Demolition crews went back to destroy everything that remained. Dozens of villages were attacked and destroyed in this manner between 1988 and 1990.

THE GULF WAR

In August 1990, Iraq invaded Kuwait and five months later, a U.S.-led Coalition launched a counterattack to expel the Iraqis. The Iraqi army retreated after setting fire to more than 500 oil wells and creating a 400-square-mile (1,000 km^2) oil spill. Coalition forces were apparently poised to follow them into Iraq, but after only 100 hours of battle, they abruptly stopped and declared a unilateral ceasefire. The Voice of America radio station broadcast a speech by President George H. W. Bush that stated: "There is another way for the bloodshed to stop: and that is for the Iraqi military and the Iraqi people to take matters into their own hands and force Saddam Hussein, the dictator, to step aside."

Encouraged by this message, the local people took up arms and a civil war erupted in the south. Small-scale skirmishes began in marshland towns in February, spreading to open warfare in Basra on March 1, 1991, when a tank gunner fired a shell into a portrait of Saddam and soldiers around him applauded jubilantly. In Najaf, a demonstration near the city's great Imam Ali Mosque became a gun battle between army deserters and Saddam's security forces. The rebels seized the shrine and Ba'ath Party members fled the city or were killed. Resistance fighters emerged from hiding and entered the cities of the south, where they were joined by masses of unarmed civilians. The rebels began to take over government buildings, especially those of the security forces and Ba'ath party headquarters.

The uprising spread rapidly to all of the larger cities of southern Iraq, including Basra, Amara, Nasriya, Karbala, Hilla, Samawa, Kut, and Diwaniya. Within a few days, the rebels controlled all three provinces encompassing the southern marshes. But the insurgents were miserably ill-equipped and inexperienced compared to the most formidable army in the Middle East, which regrouped and mounted a counteroffensive. The ceasefire prohibited Iraq from using fixed-wing aircraft below the 32nd parallel, but the Coalition allowed Saddam to continue use of helicopters. Iraq employed their gunships to strafe the rebels in their hiding places within the marshes, bombarding them with heavy artillery and spraying napalm on suspected insurgent positions.

Within weeks, the Iraqi government crushed the rebellion. According to Human Rights Watch, "When the March 1991 uprising confronted his regime with the most serious internal challenge it had ever faced, government forces responded with atrocities on a predictably massive scale. The human rights repercussions continue to be felt throughout the country. In their attempts to retake cities, and after consolidating control, loyalist forces killed thousands of unarmed civilians by firing indiscriminately into residential areas; executing young people on the streets, in homes and in hospitals; rounding up suspects, especially young men, during house-to-house searches, and arresting them without charge or shooting them en masse; and using helicopters to attack unarmed civilians as they fled the cities."

A similar situation prevailed in the north. The Kurdish population in northern Iraq also revolted against Saddam's government in the aftermath of the Gulf War, subsequently suffering atrocities and casualties similar to those of the people in the south. The international community reacted to the human disaster by establishing a Safe Haven in the north, effectively creating a semi-autonomous Kurdish state. Over the next dozen years, the Kurdish people gradually prospered, building a vigorous economy and the first successful democracy in Iraq. But no Safe Haven was established in the south, where Saddam's government exercised no restraint in crushing the revolt.

Little information about the extent of the massacre was available at the time. It was only after 2003 that hundreds of mass graves, some containing over 10,000 bodies, were discovered in southern Iraq. In 2005, the Iraqi Ministry of Human Rights estimated that between 100,000 to 200,000 southern Iraqis were killed following the 1991 rebellion.

ENTER THE BARONESS

The international community remained strangely silent about events in southern Iraq. No relief agencies, human rights advocates, or even journalists were allowed into the region, and the reports of refugees were so outlandishly ghastly that they were often discounted. Throughout the 1990s, there was only one voice consistently and vociferously decrying the plight of the Marsh Arabs: Lady Emma Nicholson, Baroness of Winterbourne and Member of the British Parliament. In the summer of 1991 she became concerned about the plight of the people in southern Iraq and she traveled to Iran, where members of the Iraqi resistance smuggled her across the border into the marshlands of Iraq. The horror of what she witnessed there would draw her into a lifelong commitment.

One of the resistance leaders who worked with her during this time was Hassan al-Sari, later to become the leader of the Hezbollah Movement in Iraq: "Our champion during those years was the Baroness Emma Nicholson. We love her tremendously. She has travelled many times to the marshes, always at very critical and dangerous times. She used to suffer from the trouble of travel just like we did. She lived with us, she walked with us—some of our strong fighters could not take this suffering like she did. She used to be close to the battles, and she has seen the attacks of the former regime on us. She saw how people died and how their houses were burned. I am at a quandary as to how to thank her for her support of the Marsh Arabs."

In December 1991 the baroness addressed the House of Commons, referring to the massacre of the marsh dwellers as a genocide equivalent to the atrocities committed under Nazi Germany or in the killing fields of Cambodia. She described people lined up in rows and run over by tanks; men pushed out of helicopters in full flight; babies killed in front of their mothers. She argued strenuously for the world to reach out and help the victims of Saddam's retribution.

She told her fellow parliamentarians that one of the worst victims that she had seen was a young boy named Amar whose family had been killed during the attacks. The boy she described no longer had a face that could smile, laugh, or even cry; his fixed, rigid visage resembled a shiny Halloween mask. Amar had been severely burned; open wounds covered his body, and his nerves had been so deeply damaged that he could barely move. The baroness managed to transport him to Britain and then launched the Amar Appeal to raise money for his medical treatment. He underwent numerous surgeries that restored limited functionality to his injuries, but he would remain horribly scarred, physically and psychologically, for life. Because Amar had no family and no prospects if returned to Iran or Iraq, Emma Nicholson adopted him as her foster child.

Following on the initial success of the appeal for Amar, the baroness was determined to continue the effort to provide services and relief for the rest of the Marsh Dwellers. The Amar Appeal evolved into the AMAR—Assisting Marsh Arab Refugees—Appeal, and she used her political clout to obtain funding to provide medical and educational assistance to marsh dweller refugees in Iran, saving the lives of many Iraqis fleeing the devastation in their country.

THE FIRST PLAN: CONVENTIONAL MILITARY CONTROL

By mid-April 1991, although Saddam had regained control of the towns and villages in southern Iraq, the resistance still raged from its sanctuary in the marshlands. Although the real fighters only numbered between 10,000 to 20,000 men, their nightly raids and works of sabotage were exacting a consistent toll on the Iraqi army and its fortifications. Saddam knew that he had to finally crush these rebels so they could not rise again.

In the marshes, word spread that the military was coming to destroy the resistance fighters, but a conventional military approach was doomed to failure in the inaccessible terrain of the swamps. The tale of one battle from the Chubayish Marsh, the fight for Umm Lilu, serves to illustrate the great difficulty faced by the élite Republican Guard as they went up against the marsh dwellers in their native habitat.

In 1992, a young marsh dweller named Abbas Dakhel watched as the army bulldozed his uncle's land near Chubayish and constructed a helicopter base. He listened as the general instructed the pilots to "get rid of the trash in the marshes, not only the fighters but even kill those who are supporting them. Your job is to level them to the ground."

Abbas and his friends were appalled. "Before 1991 we had some suffering, life was tough and the government was always on top of us, but we were still living; then it was harassment, but this had become extermination," he told me in an interview in 2008. Before this time, he had never been part of the resistance, but he couldn't watch while his people were massacred, so he sold the family's cow to buy a Kalashnikov and joined other young men in the marshes to prepare for the arrival of the troops. "We fought to retain our way of life, to be able to make a living, and our enemy was the government. The government picked the fight, we just wanted to live. We knew we couldn't destroy the government, we knew it was unwinnable, but we still had to fight."

The government troops came in a large convoy of *balam* outfitted with heavy artillery and mounted machine guns. A dozen helicopter gunships provided cover overhead. Hundreds of soldiers stormed in, hunting for the resistance fighters. Abbas and 50 other friends crouched in the reeds surrounding a small lake known as Umm Lilu, cradling makeshift weapons, some of them as old as World War I. With only their heads above the chilly water, the men watched silently as the troops moved through the marsh, finding no one to attack because some of the soldiers had given the resistance warning. After a few hours, the unit decided to return to their base, and the boats headed back into the waiting trap.

At a pre-arranged signal, Abbas and his friends opened fire. The soldiers immediately swerved the boats around to return the fire, but they were not experienced with the notoriously unstable watercraft made even more top-heavy by the mounted guns. Many of the boats capsized, and the most of the soldiers—peasants and city boys— couldn't swim. The rebels fired at the drowning soldiers from the edge of the clearing, then swam underwater to another location before releasing another volley. The soldiers must have thought that they were being fired upon by hundreds of invisible men. The helicopters returned, but in the melee beneath them they couldn't tell friend from foe; while the aircraft hovered overhead, the rebels managed to shoot one down with a couple of rocket-propelled grenades. The first and only battle in the Chubayish Marshes ended in a humiliating defeat for the Iraqi army.

PLAN TWO: FORCED EMIGRATION

After losses such as this, the government realized that they would never defeat the resistance fighters if they were assisted by locals who could use the environment to such great advantage. The military campaign thus began to focus on attacking the marsh dwellers, regardless of whether they were suspected of helping the resistance movement. The propaganda against the marsh dwellers began with a series of articles in the Ba'ath party newspaper, *al-Thawra*, attacking the *ma'dan* by falsely labeling them as immoral, "monkey-faced people" who were not "real Iraqis" but descendants of slaves.

The army installed checkpoints at key access sites and harassed everyone entering and leaving the marshes. The lucky ones were simply beaten and relieved of their possessions; the unlucky ones were arrested and tortured. The army then installed mounted machine guns on bridges over the channels leading into the marshes, firing randomly at the *mashuf* passing below. Fishermen still found ways to slip into the marshes, so the army began watching for their lights at night and strafing the nearby reeds the next day. It became almost impossible to earn a living from the marshlands, but still some villages remained, because the people knew no other way of life. They had no choice.

Eventually, little food could be obtained from the marsh, and the people became dependent on ration cards for their sustenance. Anyone suspected of resistance against the government, however—even anyone related to a person suspected of harboring resentment against the government—had their ration card revoked. Entire villages were denied food supplies as punishment for real or suspected crimes.

In preparation for their final operation, the government posted signs around the periphery of the marsh forbidding entry. Helicopters circled over the marshes, using loudspeakers to instruct the population to leave immediately. Most of the remaining marsh dwellers obeyed the commands and migrated out of the marsh. Those who disobeyed were slaughtered in their homes when the gunships returned and discharged rockets and heavy artillery into the reed dwellings. The helicopters hovered overhead, waiting to mow down any inhabitant who tried to escape. After it was clear that all the people had been killed, the army came in and burned the villages. Hundreds of settlements were destroyed in this final campaign against the marsh dwellers.

INCARCERATION OF INFANTS

Thousands of stories can be told of the suffering endured by the marsh dwellers during this period of time. A typical example is that of the tribe of Sheikh Lazem, the head of a small clan of marsh dwellers living on the edge of Abu Zirig Marsh who spoke to me in 2008 about the troubles of this time. When the army came to destroy their village, the men reacted instinctively; in the ensuing gun battle, several soldiers were killed. The army retreated and returned with reinforcements and heavy artillery. They herded the villagers into a small enclosure and forced them to watch as their huts were destroyed. Then all 75 families, including women and children, were taken to jail in Nasriya. The men were subjected to what was known as first-degree torture, which involved tying the hands behind the back and hanging them from their arms for 48 hours; this method dislocated the shoulder joints and caused horrific, enduring pain. Then the torturer, nicknamed "The Shovel," began the second-degree treatment, which entailed more painful techniques such as beating the soles of the feet with gravel-filled bags and applying electric shock to the testicles. In the women's quarters, conditions were not much better, although they were spared torture. Influenza raged throughout the cramped, unsanitary cells and medical treatment was withheld. The women spent their nights lying on their sides, head to toe, as children wailed and shrieked with excruciating ear infections.

After six months, all the prisoners were released. Lazem rushed to hold his children, who looked at him impassively through their tears. He asked them again and again how they were but they failed to respond. All three of his children, including his son who had just reached seven months, had gone permanently deaf.

THE FINAL SOLUTION: DESTROY THE MARSHES

Even with all of the villages gone, resistance fighters remained in the marsh, subsisting on what little was left of its natural resources. The regime decided to remove this source of support and began to use chemical weapons against the wildlife of the marshes. The people of the area report helicopters releasing canisters over the marshes and white smoke rising from the area; afterwards they found piles of dead birds downwind of the smoke. The targets were usually open-water ponds where large flocks of migratory water birds settled. The locals then began to find clear, clean lakes full of dead fish that had obviously been poisoned.

But killing the wildlife was only a temporary measure; what Saddam intended was the complete destruction of the entire wetland ecosystem. He placed his cousin in charge of the program—Ali Hassan al-Majid, known as "Chemical Ali" to Iraqis for his role in gassing the Kurdish population during the 1980s. Al-Majid commanded the Ministry of Irrigation to develop a scheme to drain the marshlands. Their engineers drew up a plan for draining most of the marshes while leaving wetlands across much of the Central Marshes intact for the purpose of flood control. Al-Majid was not satisfied, and when the civil engineers refused to comply, he commanded his military engineers to revise the plan so that all the marshes would be dried.

The final plan called for the construction of hundreds of miles of canals and levees, huge earthworks and dams. The project would cost tens of millions of dollars during a time when Iraq was under economic sanctions, when the nation could not even afford to feed its own people. Completion within the specified time frame would require the dedication of every single piece of earth-moving and construction equipment in Iraq. Saddam demanded its immediate implementation.

First, the engineers addressed the Main Outfall Drain, a structure that received polluted waste water trickling from the irrigated wheat and barley fields of central Iraq. This drain had been initially designed to reduce the buildup of salts, fertilizers and other chemicals in the agricultural fields and discharge this waste into the Gulf, yet funds had never been found for its completion, so it dumped the polluted water into the marshlands instead. The Iraqi regime pushed construction crews to work 24 hours a day to complete the project in a record nine months, extending the canal an additional 100 miles (160 km) and depriving the Central and Hammar Marshes of even this low-quality water. In honor of their leader, the Main Outfall Drain was renamed "Saddam's River."

DESTRUCTION OF THE CENTRAL MARSHES

Next, the engineers set about draining the Central Marshes, focusing on diverting stream flow away from the marshes. In an area with essentially no rain and an extremely high rate of evaporation, the engineers expected rapid desiccation of the marshes once the flow of the river was shut off. The main supply of water to the Central Marshes was the Tigris River. Near Amara, the Tigris divides into several smaller channels that flow southward through rice fields and then into the marshlands. The flow of water through these distributary channels had long been controlled by regulators that the regime had already closed. But silt had collected behind the regulators and rendered them useless as the water just flowed over them. Even after large earthen dykes were constructed across the ends of the channels, water still reached the marshlands. So the regime constructed the "Crown of Battles" canal, branching off from the Tigris north of Amara, to divert some of the Tigris water into the Sanaf seasonal marsh; this decreased the flow of the Tigris into the Central Marshes but did not dry them.

Finally, the regime constructed a canal that acted as a huge moat

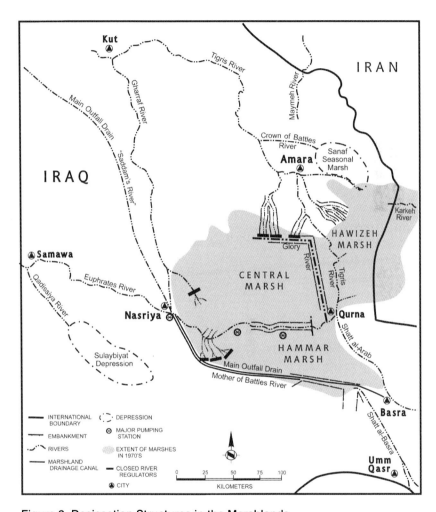

Figure 3. Desiccation Structures in the Marshlands

between the rice fields and the Central Marshes. By late 1994, all of the water flowing south from the agricultural area was intercepted by this mile-wide (1.6 km) "Glory Canal." The channel flowed eastward along the northern edge of the marshes for 25 miles (40 km) before abruptly turning south. Through this second leg, the canal was contained by earthen dykes 100 feet (30 m) wide, extending up to 30 feet (9 m) high. This channel paralleled the Tigris for another 30 miles, finally debouching into the Euphrates River. The quantity of water discharged from the Glory Canal into the Euphrates was so great that it caused the river to reverse its flow back into the Central Marshes, forcing the regime to construct a dam (known as the "7/12") on the Euphrates upstream of its intersection with the Glory Canal to maintain its down-gradient flow toward the Shatt al-Arab and the Gulf.

The Central Marshes also received a limited supply of water from the Euphrates during floods, when water from the swollen river would overtop its natural levees and flow northward. To seal off this source, the government constructed more than 100 miles (160 km) of artificial levees along both the left and right banks of the Euphrates as it passed through the marshlands.

Eliminating the flow of river water into the marshes did not provide the immediate results that the government desired, because groundwater continued to seep beneath the regulators and canals and supply the reeds with moisture through their roots. The regime therefore designed a series of drainage canals through the Central Marshes and imported dozens of giant 450-horsepower pumps to drain every last drop of water from the marsh.

Still, the resistance fighters hid amongst the dried reeds and pestered the army with frequent small skirmishes; in 1995 they even managed to dynamite a breach in the levees of the Euphrates that allowed some water back into the marshes. The army set fires in the marshes to rid the resistance of this cover, and hundreds of square miles of dried vegetation and wildlife went up in flames. Traditionally, marsh dwellers burned the reeds every winter to encourage new growth of green shoots to feed their water buffalo. But when the soil is wet, the reeds only burn down to the ground; the fire is contained in a small area, allowing much of the wildlife to escape. Now there was no water, and the roots of the reeds began to burn. The fires smoldered deep underground for months, charring every living organism, extinguishing any hope of regeneration.

DESTRUCTION OF THE HAMMAR MARSHES

The Hammar Marshes were the second ecosystem to be targeted for destruction. Stream flow in the Euphrates had already decreased markedly when Turkey began infilling the reservoir behind its giant Ataturk Dam in 1990, but two years later the dam was releasing water again. As an initial measure, the Iraqi government ordered all the regulators on the Euphrates' distributaries closed. Water was not allowed to flow into the rice fields or the numerous small villages downstream, leaving 500,000 people without a supply of drinking water.

Next the regime built a connection from the Euphrates into the Main Outfall Drain and diverted a portion of its flow into "Saddam's River." But the added flow caused the agricultural drainage water to back up into the Central Marshes, so the 40-mile (64 km) "Qadissiya River," was constructed to take water from the Euphrates and discharge it to a desert depression, creating a vast, useless lake. The depression could not hold the continued flow of the Euphrates, however, so the regime constructed the "Mother of Battles" canal that flowed parallel to the Main Outfall Drain and diverted water from the Euphrates into the new canal, bypassing the marshes.

The effect of these projects was to reduce the flow of the Euphrates to less than 10% of its original value, yet still groundwater seeped into the wetlands and sustained the reeds, so as with the Central Marshes, an extensive network of drainage ditches was dug in the Hammar Marsh and huge pumps were brought in to suck the last drops of water from the land. Finally, the dried reeds were burned.

Then another problem arose: tamarisk began to grow where reeds had once thrived. Tamarisk is a desert shrub, native to the Middle East, with roots that can extend down to 100 feet (30 m). The resistance fighters began to use the tamarisk for cover and were able to gain strength; in one operation after the marshes were dried, they killed 51 leaders of the Ba'ath party. So the government employed dozens of bulldozers to raze hundreds of square miles of tamarisk shrubs. The regime decided to give large tracts of this "reclaimed" land to loyal members of the Ba'ath party, supplying them with tractors and seed, in a strategy designed to prevent the original owners from demanding their property back. But nothing grew on the salty soil, and within a few years the "farms" lay abandoned.

NOT A DROP TO DRINK

In 1998, Ali Shaheen became the General Director of Irrigation for the governorate of Dhi Qar. When he arrived at his post, he discovered that more than a thousand square miles (2,600 km^2) of marshland in his governorate had been desiccated and the majority of the marshland people displaced from their original communities. The situation distressed him; although he was born in Baghdad, his family was originally from the marshes. He remembered his childhood holidays in the wetlands as sweet interludes of peace and calm.

But Shaheen had no aspirations to restore his beloved marshlands; people were dying from lack of water and his only concern was getting drinking water delivered to their villages. Water comes into Dhi Qar from the Euphrates River and the Gharraf, which is a branch of the Tigris River. Water from the Euphrates is suitable for agriculture, but its salinity by the time it reached Nasriya is too high for drinking water, so the Gharraf was the only natural source of drinking water available to the local population. Between 1991 and 1998, the central government had reduced its flow to a fraction of its natural capacity. Then a severe drought hit the region in 1998 and 1999, and the flow through the Gharraf ceased altogether and no water was flowing into the few remaining marshland towns such as Islah, Fuhud, and Chubayish.

Shaheen consequently asked the military governor for permission to dredge the river so that enough water would flow through to provide drinking water for the remote communities in the dried marshes. The governor refused. In an interview with me in 2008, Shaheen said, "He was willing to sacrifice the people, but he was not willing to do anything that could potentially return water to the dried marshes."

In Chubayish the situation was truly desperate. After the Euphrates ran dry, the central government had dug a ditch from the Gharraf to the town, dubbed the "Gift from the Leader Canal." Now even that ditch was dry and the people were forced to buy drinking water from tankers that drove in with water from Nasriya. Those without ration cards were not allowed to buy water, so they went out to the dry riverbed and dug wells; after twenty feet (6 m) the hole filled with a viscous blue fluid that burned in their throats like stinging ants.

The situation in the Hammar Marsh was equally desperate. After the marshlands were completely dry, the government had ordered the people back to their former communities, where a small amount of water would be allowed to reach them through the distributaries of the Euphrates. But Shaheen found that the salinity of this water was eight parts per thousand, when one part per thousand was the maximum allowable limit for human drinking water. "The water was so saline that the water buffalo were turning blind from drinking it. Palm trees were dying, and these trees are adapted to the desert so the problem was clear."

Shaheen requested permission from the military governor to increase the water flow through the distributaries to decrease its salinity and provide potable water to these towns. As a punishment for making the request, he was thrown in jail for a week. When he was released, he sent a letter to the Ministry of Irrigation in Baghdad, asking for a technical committee to come and investigate the problem, and they reached the same conclusion.

"But the minister knew that the military governor did not want any water to reach the marshlands: drying the marshlands was more important to the regime than providing drinking water to the people. So the minister stated that I would be held personally responsible for any drop of water that reached the marshes. It was one of the hardest decisions in my life, but in the end I decided that I had to make this sacrifice."

Shaheen let the water back in and the salinity decreased. Two months later, the ministry reversed their decision and ordered the flow reduced again. Conditions worsened and there was no way to survive, so the people migrated out. Some of the stronger clans moved upstream along the Euphrates, searching for small wetlands where they could find fodder for their buffalo or reeds to weave. The truly devastated migrated to the city slums where they found little work to sustain themselves.

DEATH OF THE LAST REFUGE

The Hawizeh Marsh on the Iran/Iraq border served as a natural hindrance to foreign invasion, and was therefore the last marsh area slated for destruction by Saddam's regime. On the Iraqi side, it is fed by the Tigris River, which breaks into distributaries that flow across a rice-growing region before seeping into the marshes. On the Iranian side, it is fed by the Karkheh River.

To begin draining the Central Marshes, the regime had constructed the "Crown of Battles" canal to divert water from the Tigris into the Sanaf seasonal marsh north of Hawizeh, and this reduced some of the water flow into the marsh. Then a huge earthen dyke was constructed across the middle of Hawizeh, bisecting it, and another canal was constructed just north of the dyke to drain water from the marsh back into the Tigris, leaving the southern half of Hawizeh to dry.

Iraq could not, however, stop the flow of the Karkheh River emanating from Iran, which continued to sustain the northern half of Hawizeh. With unfortunate timing, in 1995 Iran began construction of a dam on the Karkheh. In 2000, flow from the Karkheh into Iraq was completely halted as the Karkheh reservoir began to be filled. Hawizeh Marsh slowly became drier and drier, and by December 2002, there were no open water bodies, no green marshes, only dried marsh vegetation. Hawizeh had ceased to exist.

That winter, a large flock of migratory waterfowl flew in from northern Asia, searching for their usual wintering grounds. They circled the area without finding their favored habitat—small ponds surrounded by reed beds. The birds finally settled in the only body of water that could be found, the highly polluted, lifeless water overflowing from the Main Outfall Drain.

Within a day the ducks had gone blind, and the local people went in and collected them by hand for a final feast upon nature's bounty.

The last forlorn remnant of the Mesopotamian Marshes was gone.

3. CRADLE OF CIVILIZATION

*"The holy house, a house of the gods in a holy place, had not been made,
no reed had sprung up, no tree had been created ... all lands were sea.
The spring which was in the sea was a water pipe. Then was Eridu made
... Marduk laid a reed frame on the face of the waters. He created dirt and
poured it out by the reed frame, that he might cause the gods to dwell in
the habitation of their hearts' desire. He formed mankind ... he created the
Tigris and Euphrates ... [and] the lands of the marshes and the swamps."*
—Babylonian Creation Myth (ca. 1200 BC)

By the late 1990s, it appeared that the Mesopotamian Marshlands
had disappeared forever. Yet in nature, change does not follow a
unidirectional line but pulses rhythmically at different timescales—the
daily ebb and flow of the tides, the seasonal migrations of fish and fowl,
the climatic swings between flood and drought. Saddam's devastation
of the marshlands was but a moment in time, a moment that vanishes
when viewed against the vast backdrop of time in the marshlands.

In the beginning, there were wetlands. The Babylonian creation
story "Enuma Elish" evokes distant memories of a coastal lagoon
where the ocean's brine was sweetened by fresh water seeping from
underground. According to this ancient legend, all matter was born
from water: salt water was the female god Tiamat, fresh water was the
male god Apsu. Marduk, the god of light and regeneration, conquered
the chaos of Tiamat and afterward created a dwelling place for the gods
using the millennia-old technique still employed by marsh dwellers
today: in the shallow waters of the lagoon, he cut sturdy reeds and
formed a fenced enclosure that he then filled with soil. This island of
earth would serve as the place of the gods' delight, in the midst of the
bounty of the reed-filled lagoon.

After the earth was formed, ancient legend tells us that Enki (later
known as Ea), the god of water, created the remainder of the world in

a sequence that emphasizes the importance of the wetland ecosystem to the ancient Sumerians. First he filled the Tigris with his life-giving semen which turned to fresh, sparkling water, and appointed a god referred to as the "canal inspector" to take care of the rivers. Next he created the marshland and the canebrake, supplied them with fish and reeds and appointed a deity "who loves fish" to safeguard this ecosystem. Only then did he turn to the solid earth and its needs: he called forth the cultivated fields, filled them with grains and vegetables, and appointed a farmer as their god. Finally he fabricated the cities, their population sustained by the dual supports of the wetland and agrarian food supplies.

Agriculture and the natural ecosystem have often seemed mutually exclusive enterprises. Throughout human history, man has sacrificed the bounty of the Mesopotamian Marshlands in the name of progress. Empire after empire has drained the marshes for agricultural gain or for military control, yet each of these empires has ultimately collapsed. In the land where civilization was born, civilizations have failed with regularity, and with every failure, the marshlands have been reborn.

PREHISTORIC FORMATION OF THE MARSHLANDS

To fully understand the importance of marshlands to the growth of civilization, we must go back 20,000 years to the apex of the most recent glacial period of the Ice Ages, when the world was a very foreign place. Most of northern Eurasia lay beneath hundreds of feet of ice. The oceans, much of their water locked on land as ice, stood almost 400 feet lower than today. Southern Iraq[5] was covered with arid grasslands unrelieved by wetlands, while streams crossed the dry plains through deeply incised channels, bypassing the parched steppe and discharging their flow directly to the Indian Ocean. The ocean had entirely receded from the Gulf, and the broad valley would have been flowing with abundant fresh water from rivers and artesian springs.

Around 15,000 years ago, the warming climate began to melt the vast ice sheets and they released enormous torrents of water, perhaps twenty times greater than today, and extensive river systems developed across Iraq, eroding and then depositing their sediment load over the

---

[5] The country of Iraq, of course, did not yet exist; in the interests of brevity we will ask the reader to mentally insert "present-day" at each mention of a modern country.

valleys on their way to the sea. The influx of fresh water from the melting glaciers began to rapidly refill the ocean, decreasing the salinity of the coastal waters, and slowly altering their ecosystems. Shorelines inched inexorably landward.

The rising seas began to flood the flat-lying Gulf, creating a coastal mosaic of shallow-water lagoons, mudflats and fresh- and saltwater marshes. Aquatic organisms quickly adapted to the intermingling of rivers and sea, and the fertile waters teemed with abundant life. By 8000 BC the Gulf was completely flooded with marine water.

Around 7000 BC, numerous human settlements began to appear on the shores of the Gulf. The origin of this population remains hotly debated. Archaeologists have recently proposed that Neolithic humans occupied the relative oasis of the Gulf, through which flowed the proto-Shatt al-Arab and were potentially also dotted with freshwater springs, during the aridity of the last glacial period, and then were forced uphill to the current coastline by the rising seas. Other scholars propose that humans migrated to this location from elsewhere. At any rate, we know that these "fisher/gatherers of the Arab littoral" who settled along the Gulf coast around 7000 BC lived similar lifestyles to that of the earliest Sumerians, building their homes from reeds and mud, subsisting on fish, shellfish, turtles, eggs, small birds and wild greens. They even fashioned boats of reeds and rowed them along the length of the Gulf.

By 6000 BC the mounting ocean had flooded the Gulf and advanced into southern Iraq, forming a shallow lagoon that covered essentially the same area as today's Mesopotamian Marshlands. Rivers continued to carry away the sediment disgorged by the melting glaciers in the Taurus Mountains to the north, silting up the incised stream channels and allowing floodwaters to spill over the plains, creating vast seasonal freshwater wetlands throughout the Mesopotamian valley. As the land flattened near the coast, the rivers slowed and branched off into numerous small channels, creating deltas and freshwater wetlands at the edge of the shallow lagoon. Seawater mixed with the fresh, yielding a brackish lagoon where thick stands of reeds developed, sheltering schools of darting fish and attracting flocks of migrating waterfowl.

The fisher/gatherers of the Arab littoral followed the rising seas into southern Mesopotamia. Circling the shoreline of the lagoon, they found the rich deltaic environment where they built their reed huts on the higher land of the river's levees and paddled their reed canoes down its distributaries to fish and hunt within the shallow waters. Thus began the Ubaid period.

In northern Mesopotamia, meanwhile, humans had been living in the hills of northern Iraq since 9000 BC. There, they subsisted on wild goat, sheep, and deer; they gathered the emmer wheat and two-hulled barley growing wild on the local hill slopes, and grain gradually became the staple of their diet. Population growth propelled them in a continuous southward migration, following the flow of the rivers. They brought with them wheat and barley seeds which they sowed in their new land, reaping an abundant harvest that continued to increase their population. But as they progressed southward the climate became drier; with insufficient rainfall, they could only plant grain within the river valleys where they learned to dig canals to irrigate their fields. But the agricultural potential of the upper river valleys was limited both by the narrowness of the valleys themselves and by the timing of the river floods, which came too early for the growing season of wheat and barley.

The real agrarian revolution occurred around 5000 BC when the farming technology of the north encountered the delta of the south. The lower Euphrates valley was the perfect environment for the cultivation of grain. In the delta, the river branched into small distributaries that served as natural irrigation canals for the fields formed by clearing the reed beds. As these distributaries eventually silted up and became useless, the local farmers cleaned them out, straightened and extended them, eventually turning the practice of "wild" irrigation into a purposeful, man-made construct. These people, whom we now call Sumerians, cleared huge plots of land and placed them under cultivation, yielding a surplus of grain that fueled an ever-increasing population expansion.

Archaeological evidence shows that settlements grew rapidly along the deltaic distributaries, strung out in a web-like pattern along them like eyes on a peacock's tail. It has been hypothesized that as time passed, the villages located on the main channel of the river, just upstream of its branches, would naturally tend to become more powerful as this position controlled the flow of water to the downstream distributaries. Every spring, the settlements down in the lower delta would be inundated by floodwaters, and one can easily imagine refugees gathering their meager belongings onto their reed boats and rowing upstream to the more powerful village located on the still-dry levee of the main river. There they socialized and traded their crafts and talents; there they would build an altar and pray for the floodwaters to subside.

In this way, these upstream settlements would gradually gain population and power as the altar grew into a temple with priests who demanded tithes from the surrounding lands. Craftspeople came to sell their wares and stayed: the settlement evolved into a trade center.

SUMERIAN CIVILIZATION IN THE MARSHLANDS

Around 4000 BC, one of these delta-head settlements grew into the world's first city with the epic hero Gilgamesh as its king. Uruk lay at the head of the Euphrates delta, about 40 miles (65 km) upstream of the modern-day city of Nasriya. With a population peaking at perhaps 80,000, this city is widely regarded as the birthplace of civilization. Within her walls we find the first monumental architecture, specialization of trade, standardization of industrial production, bureaucratic government, state religion and social stratification.

The Sumerian urbanites had to be supplied with food produced outside the city, and historians have long supposed that it was the surplus of grain engendered by the invention of river-fed irrigation that provided the economic base for this rapid urban expansion. Yet irrigated fields yield their crops only once per year, and river-fed agriculture tends to fail at least once per decade. Dry land farming is an extremely precarious livelihood, as the world has witnessed almost predictable cycles of widespread famine in any grassland/steppe developed for agriculture.

Recently, scholars have proposed that the economic engine for these early cities was fueled not only by the annual crop of grain but also the perennial supply of food from the adjacent marshlands. Textual and archaeological evidence shows that marshland resources were enthusiastically exploited by the ancient cities long after agriculture had been established. For example, we find on one Sumerian tablet an account of foodstuffs delivered from the marshes to a single palace, documenting the provision of 16,000 large birds, 18,000 little birds, 152,000 bird eggs, and 5,000 turtles and their eggs over a three-year period.

The vast majority of Sumerian workers ate dried fish as their main source of protein, mainly derived from the shallow, tranquil waters of the marsh and lagoon. Government authorities controlled and leased fishing rights to commercial fisherman, who generally captured their prey with nets, although traps and fishing lines were also mentioned in Sumerian texts. But either fishing became less important over time, or over-harvesting depleted the biodiversity in the marshes and rivers, for although over 50 different kinds of fish were mentioned in writings dating before 2500 BC, only half a dozen are mentioned in texts from the later Sumerian period.

Pigs ran wild in the marshes and were domesticated by the marsh dwellers, who slaughtered them primarily for their lard rather than their meat; southern Mesopotamia lacked a significant indigenous source of vegetable oil. Pasturage in Mesopotamia was too sparse to support the high-energy needs of cattle, so larger livestock were raised exclusively in the marshes, where reed shoots supplied additional fodder. Sumerian cylinder rolls have been found with bucolic scenes of cattle being milked in the marshes beside their reed byres; nearby, workers are depicted churning the milk for butter and patting out cakes of cheese. These herds were raised primarily for dairy production rather than meat. Likewise, only the élite ate the flesh of the goats and sheep herded by nomadic tribes along the fringes of the marshland, although wool production from these animals also provided vital input for an urban textile industry.

Dates grown in the marshes provided the main source of sugar for the Sumerians and were exported as their major cash crop. Date palms lined every distributary channel of the delta. The Sumerians invented shade tree gardening, planting a layer of fruit trees below the palms that shielded them from excessive sun and wind; a final tier of vegetables flourished beneath the fruit trees.

In the marshlands, the architectural style of the fisher/gatherers of the Arab littoral continued to flourish. Excavations in the major Sumerian cities typically encounter reed-based architecture at the deepest levels of occupation, replaced by mud-brick construction as cities developed in later periods. Although natural materials such as reeds are not well-preserved in the archaeological record, numerous Sumerian cylinder seals depict reed-built structures ranging from simple livestock shelters to large, arched edifices with prominent geometric decoration achieved by intricate designs in the woven cane, indicating that the architectural use of reeds continued throughout the Sumerian period. The design of the reed-based structures proved most suitable for air circulation and comfort in the arid environment, although mud-brick homes prevailed in the towns and cities, where the ever-present threat of fire discouraged such flammable structures. The perennial resources of the marshlands—reeds, fish, birds, eggs, dairy, dates and lard—provided vital sustenance for the swelling urban population, yet grain cultivation continued to advance and

Figure 4. Ancient Civilizations of Mesopotamia

proliferate because cereals were cheap and easy to produce. Around 3500 BC the warm and humid climate became cooler and dryer, and farmers in northern Mesopotamia began to move south toward the lower Euphrates Valley. Observing how the Sumerians used the distributaries of the delta to irrigate their crops, they began to apply the same technology upstream, using natural flood breaks, or crevasse splays, that branched off from the main river channel upstream. The industrious farmers deepened, straightened, and extended the natural distributaries and dug new outlets from the main channel, and soon the lower Euphrates Valley was crossed by a herringbone grid of canals.

The Sumerian lagoon lay at the nexus between riparian and maritime traffic, and the city of Ur on its northern shore grew into a bustling entrepôt. Sumerian trade spread their civilization: cylinder seals from Ur have been found in excavations as far away as the Indus Valley. The flower of Sumerian civilization, Ur and its merchants dominated Sumer for almost a thousand years. From its Royal Cemetery we find evidence of incredible luxury: Queen Puabi's elaborate headdress of gold hammered in the delicate shapes of water lilies and willow leaves, reminiscent of the esteemed marshland setting; opulent jewelry of imported carnelian and lapis lazuli alongside simple vessels of polished conch shells. The famous sculpture 'Ram Caught in a Thicket' was buried near her grave, along with golden statues of leopards and enameled harps.

THE FALL OF THE SUMERIANS

The Sumerians had dominated southern Mesopotamia for thousands of years in relatively peaceful co-existence with their Semitic neighbors, the Akkadians, to the north. That concord was shattered around 2350 BC by Sargon the Great, who formed the world's first multiethnic, centrally controlled empire that stretched from Iraq to Turkey and from Iran to the Mediterranean Sea.

Sargon's dynasty controlled Mesopotamia for around a century and a half and then collapsed almost as fast as it had developed, initiating a pattern of development and decline that would characterize every empire thereafter. Akkad was entirely dependent upon the agricultural systems of the region, especially the farmlands of Sumer, which had a yield of 30 grains returned for each grain sown, making it even more productive than modern farming. The food surplus enabled the growth of the highest population densities in the world at the time, thus yielding a critical military advantage to Akkad.

The Sumerian fields, however, were entirely dependent on irrigation, and with each application of water, a small amount of salt stayed behind, forming a saline residue. Without proper drainage of the fields, the soils became progressively saltier, decreasing the total yields. Soil salinization is described at length in Sumerian texts, and eventually the agricultural fields were converted from wheat to the more salt-tolerant barley.

Around 2100 BC there was an abrupt global climate change, with increased temperatures and decreased rainfall across the Middle East. The irrigated agricultural economy collapsed and there was widespread abandonment of cities across the Akkadian Empire. The refugees wandered the river valleys with bone-thin livestock, their cities left to be covered with wind-swept sand.

But although man-made agriculture failed, the natural ecosystem kept producing. As the irrigation canals went unattended, the water flowed instead to the marshlands and the economy of the old Sumerian cities revived. Once again the city of Ur ruled over the lands of Sumer, but for only a brief period. Ur finally fell around 2000 BC when a major flood shifted the channel of the Euphrates River, leaving the city dry. For the next few hundred years, power over the area shifted between several other Sumerian city-states, primarily Larsa.

The aridity continued, driving refugees and nomadic herders closer to the settled river valleys, causing increased conflict between the pastoralists and the farmers. Semitic tribes from the west encroached upon the lands of Sumer and Akkad, which were finally taken over in 1800 BC by Amorites invading from the Syrian Desert. From their capital Babylon, on the banks of the middle Euphrates River, they ruled over the combined empire of Akkad and Sumer for 400 years.

SEALAND UNDER THE BABYLONIANS

The Babylonians called the region "Sealand," and within its watery landscape marsh dwellers carried on a lifestyle already thousands of years old, inherited from the Neolithic fisher/gatherers of the Arab littoral, a culture that had managed to persevere despite the dual pressures of agriculture and urbanization. The upstream diversion of irrigation water was a constant and increasing threat to the sustainability of this fragile ecosystem and yet the wetlands flourished. But now a new threat to the habitat emerged: the need for central government control of the region.

Babylon imposed Amorite governors over the province, but the wilderness of the reeds proved almost impossible to regulate. Foreign domination created dissidents who were forced to flee the cities; they found refuge in the dense reed beds, and the marshes developed into a sanctuary for rebels, outlaws, and criminals. During Hammurabi's reign, justice generally prevailed and the people were content to be ruled by the north, but after his death his son ruled less wisely, generating widespread dissatisfaction and revolt in the south.

Around 1700 BC, the Sealanders rebelled against Babylon and liberated the area from Amorite control, establishing the First Dynasty of Sealand. The Amorites regrouped and attacked the rebels, forcing them back into the marshes which proved impenetrable to the army. The cause was taken up by Hammurabi's grandson, who realized that the Amorites could never achieve victory in the wetlands, so he ordered the construction of a dam on the Tigris to divert water away from the marshes and dry them out, hoping to thereby flush out the rebel fighters by denying them the shelter of the reeds.

The first documented plan to desiccate the marshlands in order to achieve military control failed, since water enters the marshlands not only through surface rivers, but also seeps up from vast underground reserves. Unable to stem the flow of groundwater, the Babylonians were forced to admit defeat, and Sealand remained a semi-autonomous state for the remainder of the Babylonian era, even once again dominating Babylon briefly around 1000 BC during the Second Dynasty of Sealand.

During this time, the geography of southern Sumer changed gradually yet inexorably. For thousands of years, the rivers antecedent to the modern-day Tigris and Euphrates had debouched into the shallow brackish-water lagoon that covered southern Mesopotamia, forming deltas that had built up gradually, then avulsed and reformed in another area. The great cities of the Sumerians—Eridu, Ur, Uruk, Lagash, Girsu, and Larsa—were all built on these waterways. These deltas gradually pushed the shoreline further and further south, eventually abutting against the deltas of two other great rivers—the Karkheh and the Karun from Iran—encroaching from the southeast. The combined deltas created a bottleneck that effectively choked off the marine waters of the Gulf, and the shallow lagoon slowly evolved into a freshwater marsh.

Apsu finally conquered Tiamat, and the modern Mesopotamian Marshlands[6] were formed.

CHALDEA UNDER THE ASSYRIANS

Northern Mesopotamia had been ruled by the Assyrians since the fall of the Ur dynasty in 2000 BC. The Assyrians were a highly militaristic society, and by 750 BC they had built up the largest army in the region. They began a series of conquests, eventually expanding their empire to encompass all of the Middle East, from Egypt to the Caspian Sea, including the marshlands of southern Babylonia.

The Assyrians called the people of the marshlands *Kaldu* or Chaldean. Little is known about the origin of the Chaldeans other than that they spoke a Semitic language and began to be mentioned as residing in the marshes around the 9th century BC. Whether the name "Chaldean" is simply another name for Sealander, or if it represents a population newly immigrated to the marshlands, remains unclear.

We do know that the Chaldeans, like the Sealanders, constantly threatened the sovereignty of the central government. In 710 BC, in an attempt to end the festering revolt, the Assyrian leader Sargon II launched an attack in the marshes east of the Tigris River (the area known today as the Hawizeh Marsh). The Chaldeans, led by Marduk-apla-idinna, protected their capital city by digging a canal from a nearby river so that water flooded the plain, turning the metropolis into an island fortress. Eventually Sargon II conquered the city, but the Chaldean warriors fled into the nearby marshes where the army's tactics proved useless to rout them. To force the fugitives out of hiding, the Assyrians diverted one of the rivers, flooding the area and successfully forcing the fighters onto dry land. But Sargon II did not capture Marduk-apla-iddina, who fled to the kingdom of Elam, located in what is now southwestern Iran.

When Sargon II was succeeded by his son Sennacherib, Marduk-apla-iddina came out of exile and again incited a rebellion against the

---

[6] The time period during which these changes began and ended remains unknown; the transition from a brackish/marine to a freshwater/brackish environment may have occurred as early as 2500 BC or as late as 1500 BC. Some researchers have proposed even earlier and even later dates.

Assyrian empire. Sennacherib marched southward; once again his enemy retreated to the marshlands. An evocative bas-relief frieze from his palace at Nineveh illustrates the battle. A forest of towering reeds (rendered in sufficient detail to identify their genus as *Phragmites*) envelops the scene; narrow channels curve between the reeds, teeming with large carp and an occasional snapping crab. Hidden within the reed beds the marsh dwellers cower, crouching on small rafts made of bundled reeds. The Assyrians stand on large canoes, also constructed of bundled reeds, resolutely volleying spears and arrows into the reeds to seek their prey.

Even after this extensive hunt, Marduk-apla-iddina was not captured. The victorious Sennacherib returned to Assyria with a treasure trove of biological specimens from the unique environment of southern Babylon and put to work the 200,000 captives that he had taken from the marshes to construct the world's first botanical park and wildlife preserve at his castle in Ninevah.

The Assyrian empire came to an end in 625 BC. After that, the Chaldeans ruled Babylon for nearly a century in what is known as the "Neo-Babylonian Era," during which King Nebuchadnezzar built the fabled Hanging Gardens of Babylon. Around 550 BC the Chaldeans lost control of Babylon and its lands were absorbed by the Persian Empire, which administered the marshlands until it fell to the Macedonians.

ENTER THE GREEKS AND ROMANS

Alexander the Great marched into Babylon in 331 BC. Intent on annexing Arabia to his dominion, he sailed down the Euphrates with a small expeditionary force to determine its viability for troop transport during the proposed invasion. But after crossing through modern-day central Iraq, the river began to branch off into ever-smaller distributaries, and some of his vessels became lost in its labyrinth windings. Eventually the channel disappeared altogether and Alexander found himself within a great swamp. The local guides informed him that these marshes harbored the burial tombs of ancient royalty (Sumerian documents refer to burial "in the reeds of Enki" as a final disposition reserved only for the élite). Alexander tarried awhile in the reed beds, exploring the marshes and marveling at the ancient relics emerging from their murky waters.

But the marshlands' first instance of "ecotourism" did not end well. Alexander returned to Babylon and a few days later was stricken by a fever that became progressively worse, and within a week he was dead. Most ancient historians assumed he had been poisoned; modern forensics experts, however, believe he was bitten by a mosquito bearing the West Nile Virus while touring the marshes.

Romans followed the Greeks, and the first scientists to explore the marshes were Italian. In the early first century AD, the geographer Strabo visited the land between the two rivers, remarking on the marshes and lakes that effectively separated the Arabian Peninsula from Mesopotamia:

> " . . . for the Euphrates rises to flood-tide at the beginning of summer, beginning first to rise in the spring when the snows in Armenia melt; so that of necessity it forms lakes and deluges the ploughed lands ... the overflow of the waters, emptying into the plains near the sea, forms lakes and marshes and reed-beds, which last supply reeds from which all kinds of reed-vessels are woven. Some of these vessels, when smeared all over with asphalt, can hold water, whereas the others are used in their bare state ... The country produces larger crops of barley than any other country... but three of their tribes have no grain; and these live in marshes and are fish-eaters..."

A few decades later, Pliny the Elder wrote of "Babylon in the marshes of the Euphrates," and how the Tigris River "discharges into the Chaldean lakes, which it supplies for a distance of 70 miles (110 km). Escaping from them by a vast channel, it ... passes into the Persian Sea."

THE MESENE UNDER THE PERSIANS

Mesopotamia again fell under Persian control between 125 BC and 650 AD and the marshlands were once again subject to imposition of the human will. The Persians called the southern marshlands the Mesene, an Aramaic word retained in the modern-day name for the Maysan governorate which encompasses the Hawizeh Marshes.

Agricultural output was the backbone of the empire's economy, and irrigation works were implemented on a grand scale. Extensive canal systems, dams and weirs were constructed, and all the country's water resources were brought under central government control.

After the Persians had developed the entire central Mesopotamian valley as irrigated farmland, they looked southward at the verdant stands of reeds in the marshes and envisioned fields of grain instead. Vast stretches of former marshland were drained, the dried reeds burned and the newly-exposed soil put to the plow. The silts of the delta initially proved extremely fertile, and it must have seemed to the Persians that they had finally conquered this natural wilderness.

But the system of intensive, export-based agriculture proved unsustainable. Central control of irrigation meant that urban governors determined who would get water and when, creating fertile pastures in some areas that were previously desert and laying waste to previously-productive fields—capricious acts that spawned widespread dissatisfaction and resentment. Heavy taxation created an increasing demand for wheat and barley, transforming a diversified agricultural economy to a monoculture of grain. Soil salinization proved an intractable problem because peasants began to neglect their practice, inherited from the Sumerians, of letting a field lie fallow every third year; the overseers would not allow land to rest when it could be producing grain for export to the empire. The poorly-drained soils became increasingly salty, and the once-productive yields from Mesopotamia gradually decreased.

Nature eventually proved unconquerable. An extreme flood in 629 AD caused the Tigris River to dramatically change its course, eroding a new path through the area now known as the Central Marshes, where it wound through the countryside not as a single channel but as a series of open-water lagoons connected by narrow channels. The Euphrates River, equally engorged, burst through its dykes and levees and resumed its natural configuration, flowing through meandering channels that periodically branched into small distributaries leading into open-water lakes that subsequently drained back into a main channel, then repeating the pattern further downstream.

The powerful torrents devastated the dams, sluice gates, canals and levees that controlled the flow of irrigation water to southern Iraq. The agricultural fields formerly reclaimed from the marshes evolved once again to wetlands, and the central government offered little help in repairing the system, for a plague was ravaging the empire that would eventually kill perhaps a third of the Persian population.

The agricultural system of Mesopotamia collapsed, and gradually the marshlands reestablished themselves. The floodwaters spilling over the breached levees carried with them aquatic life of all kinds—fish, crabs, snails and clams—that quickly settled into the newly formed habitat. Otters and other predators followed, finding their prey easy to catch in the shallow waters. Gradually reeds began to sprout where once grain had grown, and clumps of pondweed floated on the water next to blooming water lilies. Flocks of migrating birds spied the shallow lakes and spiraled down to rest and breed. Slowly mammals migrated into the marshes: mice and marsh rats, deer and gazelle, leopard and lion.

And the local people returned to their roots in the marshlands to once again exploit the natural resources of reeds, fish and birds. The ecosystem's natural food web flourished and fishing once again became a primary economic activity. Historians of the time documented tremendous catches of fish that were salted and exported throughout the land.

THE BATA'IH IN THE ISLAMIC EMPIRE

The Persian Empire, weakened by the plague and the loss of its Mesopotamian breadbasket, succumbed to the influx of Muslims from the south in 636. The Arabs coming from their desert lands must have gazed in wonder at the rich green and watery land of the southern marshlands, which they called Bata'ih, meaning "lagoon." At the time, the Bata'ih stretched 200 miles (320 km) from Basra up to Babylon on the Euphrates and Kut on the Tigris. The inhabitants were almost entirely Semitic, their ethnicity dominated by Chaldeans, Arameans and Arabs who adhered to a variety of religions including Christianity, Judaism, Zoroastrianism, and Mandean; many of these Mesopotamians rapidly converted to Islam, drawn by its message of social justice and brotherhood.

The leaders of the Islamic Caliphates understood the concept of a progressive civilization as one that was constantly increasing its surplus profit. They repaired the irrigation system in the mid-Euphrates and the eastern Tigris, but the improved yields only enlarged the expectations of the empire for ever-increasing food supplies. They looked at the flooded marshlands of the Bata'ih and remembered the vast irrigated fields of wheat and barley that had dominated the landscape under the Persians.

Once again the marshes were sacrificed in the name of agricultural progress. The local governor hired a Nabatean engineer to draw up plans for draining the marshlands through an extensive series of canals and dykes. But reclaiming the marshes required intensive labor: the most egregious task was removing tons of salt-encrusted soil, which the local population proved resistant to undertaking. The problem was resolved by importing tens of thousands of slaves from the east African area of Zanj, known now as the Zanzibar region of Tanzania.

The Caliphate used this labor to greatly expand the wet cultivation of rice in the reclaimed marshlands. They were also responsible for introducing water buffalo into the region, which had a tremendous impact on the economy and physical geography of the marshlands..

Working under oppressive working conditions, and conscious of their overwhelmingly large population, the Zanj rebelled on at least three occasions between the seventh and ninth centuries. The largest slave rebellion in history lasted from 868 to 883 when the Zanj controlled the marshlands of the Tigris from Basra to Kut. The aggressive rebellion was ultimately only suppressed with the intervention of a large cavalry and navy force that included 10,000 small craft suitable for pursuing the Zanj through the marshes and canals. The victorious general commanded the fierce fighters to join his forces, but many refused and went into hiding in the marshes outside Basra.

THE MEDIEVAL MARSH ARABS

The Abbasid Caliphate ended in 1250 when Mongols invaded Iraq. Hulagu Khan, the grandson of Genghis Khan, sacked Baghdad and wreaked terrible destruction on the country's infrastructure, especially the extensive canal system that had been constructed under the Abbasids. Without human intervention, the rivers and marshes once again took their natural shape. The country was sacked again during the invasion of Tamerlane, and chaos prevailed until the Ottomans invaded from Turkey and took control of the country in 1534.

But the Ottomans did little to restore the agricultural infrastructure system, focusing on major urban areas and essentially ignoring the rural countryside. Its army rarely ventured into the marshes, and their population became even more isolated and independent from central control. Arab Bedouin tribes, fleeing from the invading Mongols and

Turks, began to settle along the edges of the marshlands, particularly along the extensive distributaries of the Tigris and Euphrates that branched out from Kut, Amara, and Nasriya. Rice cultivation had become the primary crop here after its introduction by the Persians, and many of the Bedouins settled down to farming. Gradually the tribes expanded their area of influence, enthusiastically appropriating the groves of date palms that lined the river banks and venturing into the marshlands to fish and hunt fowl.

These were the tribes that would later be known as the Marsh Arabs. While the Turks ruled the cities, the population in the rural areas increasingly relied on the strength of these tribes as a kind of quasi-government. As conflicts arose between the groups, some gained in power and influence until they ruled over large areas of the countryside. By the 17th century, the tribe of the Bani Lam had established authority over the marshes of the lower Tigris from Kut to Amara, while their rivals, the Albu Mohammed, generally controlled the Tigris marshes south of Amara. But the most powerful confederation was founded on the lower Euphrates in the Central and Hammar Marshes, where the tribes of the Bani Malik, the Ajwad and the Beni Said were united under the name Muntafiq.

Deeper within the marshes lived the *ma'dan*, a cultural designation first encountered in the writings of Ibn Battuta around 1250, yet the etymology of the word remains unknown. The *ma'dan* lived quietly throughout the Middle Ages, subsisting on their reed-based economy. European travelers such as Pietro della Valle in 1625 and Carsten Niebuhr in 1765 occasionally came near the marshlands but never truly ventured inside them, and their unique way of life remained unknown to the outside world.

The first European woman to visit the marshlands was Pauline Helfer, a passenger on the steamship Euphrates on its maiden and final voyage down its eponymous river in 1835. Helfer and her husband were amateur natural scientists and they frequently went ashore to collect biological specimens. When the ship docked overnight at a riverside village, she was nearly abducted by one of the marsh dwellers who had taken a fancy to the young woman.

The British took over Iraq after World War I and found the marshlands as difficult to control as had every other empire before them. A few British colonialists visited the marshlands, but no European spent any significant time in the unique ecosystem until Wilfred Thesiger set forth in his lone canoe.

CYCLES OF DESTRUCTION AND REBIRTH

Thus we find that the modern-day marsh dwellers are practitioners of a lifestyle that has been carried on for millennia, inheritors of traditions rooted in the beginning of human history. Their culture has been dictated by the marshland geography, their lives intricately intertwined with their environment.

The Mesopotamian Marshlands represent one of the most disturbed ecosystems on earth, but also one of the most resilient. It is certain that the marshes would be different without their human inhabitants tending their watery garden, harvesting its greenery, burning the dried reeds for rejuvenation, and herding their livestock to maintain its channels. Without the marsh dwellers, it is likely the marshes themselves would disappear, choked in their own vegetation. Yet the careful tending actions of the marsh dwellers cannot be compared to the devastation wreaked by rulers desiring control of the environment for agricultural gain or military dominance. Time and again, the marshlands have been destroyed by these rulers, and time and again they have sprouted anew. Nature is self-healing. Out of each failed civilization the natural ecosystem has been reborn, and the people fleeing the urban wastelands have found respite amidst the reeds and lagoons of the regenerated marshlands.

4. RESTORATION BY REMOTE CONTROL

The [demon]… was a mad dog attacking to kill the helpless, dripping with sweat on its flanks.… Like an accursed storm, it howled in a raucous voice; like a gigantic snake, it roared at the land. It dried up the waters of the mountains, dragged away the tamarisks, tore the flesh of the Earth and covered her with painful wounds. It set fire to the reed-beds, bathed the sky in blood, turned it inside out; it dispersed the people there. At that moment, on that day, the fields became black potash, across the whole extent of the horizon.

—The Exploits of Ninurta (ca. 1800 BC)

By the late 1990s, Saddam had largely succeeded at the enormous task of draining the Mesopotamian marshlands. In less than a decade, thousands of square miles of verdant green had been dried to salt and dust. One of the world's largest wetlands had all but disappeared, yet the world seemed to be unaware of its loss. Ludicrous as it may seem, Iraqi government officials staunchly denied the drainage project, claiming instead that the wetlands were being dried to provide more economic opportunities for the marsh dwellers. The truth was spread only by word of mouth, from Iraqi to Iraqi whispering behind closed doors.

Saddam's repressive regime was so far-reaching that even those Iraqis who had fled the country dared not speak openly about events in Iraq for fear of reprisal against family members left behind. Of course, the marsh dwellers realized that their own local marsh had been dried, and local government administrators knew about events in their own district, but they had no way to communicate with each other to form a full picture of the situation. Therefore, few people realized the full scope of the campaign to eliminate the marshes and their people.

THE AMAR APPEAL

During this time, Baroness Emma Nicholson received regular reports about the dire situation in southern Iraq from the refugees at the camps she supported in Iran. On several occasions, she addressed the British Parliament concerning the ongoing humanitarian crisis, demanding the designation of a Safe Haven in the south similar to that which had been established for the Kurdish population in the north. But no matter how passionately she described the desperate plight of the marsh dwellers, only a few newspapers covered the story and their words engendered no specific action.

No one was listening. For some reason, humanitarians and human rights activists remained apparently unmotivated to assist the marsh dwellers, so the Baroness decided to try and recruit other types of activists to her cause. In 1993 she once again addressed the House of Commons, reporting that conditions in the marshlands had become truly desperate: the wetlands were losing water fast. She emphasized the ecological impacts of marshland drainage in addition to the human disaster, hoping that environmental organizations would lend their voices to hers in demanding that both the ecosystem and its inhabitants be rescued.

She soon realized that these environmental groups wanted to see objective scientific data to support her claim that the marshlands were being deliberately drained, so she procured funding and commissioned the University of Exeter's Wetlands Ecosystems Research Group, led by Dr. Edward Maltby, to evaluate environmental conditions in the marshlands.

The Exeter scientists compared marshland conditions as shown on satellite images taken from 1984 and 1992 and concluded that significant drainage, amounting to 13% of Hammar, 27% of Hawizeh and 33% of the Central Marshes, had taken place during that time. But although the data clearly demonstrated that the marshlands were drying up, the scientists could not predict that they would be almost completely desiccated by the time the report was finally released.

The team also developed models of the hydrology of the Tigris and Euphrates Rivers; these models indicated that the planned upstream dams and irrigation schemes in Turkey and Syria, if fully implemented, would cause the complete loss of the Mesopotamian Marshlands within ten to twenty years with or without the drainage structures being constructed in southern Iraq by Saddam's government.

In the spring of 1994, AMAR Appeal released its draft report outlining the dangers to this vital ecosystem. Many newspapers and magazines covered the story and cries of horror rippled through the international environmental community.

Then the outside world stood by for six years while the marshes continued to dry.

UNEP SOUNDS THE ALARM

By 2000, the desiccation of the marshlands had begun to impact the entire region. Without the ameliorative effect of evaporative cooling from the wetlands, regional temperatures were rising. Dust storms increased in frequency and extent as the hot wind blew over the desiccated lands, eroding its fine soil and carrying the detritus hundreds of miles inland.

The environment of the Gulf suffered particularly serious consequences due to the loss of the wetlands. The marshes traditionally acted as the kidney of the Tigris and Euphrates: the rivers discharged their muddy water into the marshes, where the silt and pollutants settled, and then the cleansed water was released back to the Shatt al-Arab. Without this filtering effect, the rivers issued greater sediment and pollutant loads to the Gulf, damaging its ecosystem. The coral reefs of the Gulf, dependent on clear water for survival, suffered major bleaching events in 1996 and 1998, and toxic algal blooms became more frequent. Several economically important anadromous fish species, such as the *zobaidy* (Hilsa or Indian Shad), historically migrated into the marshlands of Iraq to spawn; lacking their accustomed spawning grounds, landings of these fish in the Gulf dramatically declined.

The countries bordering on the Gulf looked upstream for the source of these problems, and a request went out to the United Nations Environmental Program (UNEP) for an objective scientific assessment of the deleterious changes in the Gulf and their possible solution. In response, UNEP proposed a study of the entire watershed of the Tigris and Euphrates Rivers, from their headwaters in Turkey to their discharge into the Gulf. A young Iraqi-Swiss scientist at UNEP by the name of Hassan Partow heard of the proposed study and eagerly asked to serve as its leader.

Partow was born in Baghdad but spent his youth in Egypt and Yemen. He fell in love with the marshlands not by personal experience but through the descriptions of the ecosystem in the books by

Thesiger and Young. During the 1990s, he had read with dismay the few published accounts of Saddam's attempts to dry the marshes but felt powerless to assist. Learning of the environmental deterioration in the Gulf, he immediately suspected a linkage to the desiccation of the marshlands. Partow therefore requested that he begin the watershed study with an examination of the status of the Iraqi marshlands.

The problem with undertaking this inquiry lay in logistics: how could he assess the condition of the marshlands if he could not get into the country? At that time, the UN was struggling to get weapons inspectors into Iraq: asking to send in wetlands inspectors would be perceived as an unnecessary sideshow. But Partow was an expert in remote sensing analysis and he knew exactly how to approach the issue. He would be the "eyes in the sky" and rely on satellite imagery to detect changes in the landscape over Iraq.

To fully understand the transformation, he would need to compare high-resolution satellite images of the marshlands before and after Saddam's drainage projects. So he ordered the oldest (1973) and the most recent (2000) LANDSAT images of the marshes, along with data from 1990 and 1994. When he finally sat down to examine the processed images he felt as though he was embarking on a clandestine operation. Although Iraqi refugees and expatriate opposition groups claimed that the marshlands were being dried to achieve military control over the region, the Iraqi government maintained that all of its projects in the south were intended to benefit the local population. The truth had so far been difficult to discern, because Iraq had converted the marsh area into a military zone, denying access to humanitarian or human rights groups. Even the people living in southern Iraq could not fully comprehend the status of the land around them. Now Partow would learn the truth.

The 1973 image glowed in a rich mosaic of deep red and rich brown, swirled with ribbons of cobalt and splashes of turquoise. In his mind's eye, he could translate every color on the image to an ecosystem on land: the deep red colors meant lush, verdant vegetation, the dark blues indicated deep, cold water, while light blue suggested shallower, warmer lakes; the sandy desert showed up as light brown, and cold grey indicated the concrete of the urban cities. He marveled at the vast extent of the wetlands, the graceful sweep of a landscape exquisite even from outer space.

Then he turned to the 2000 image and the disparity stunned him. He couldn't locate the marshes. At first he thought there was some error, perhaps someone had provided him with the wrong images, but closer observation gave him his bearings: this was the correct geographic region. But the lush landscape of the marshes had been completely replaced by a dismal palette of grey and beige. All that remained of the vast expanse of wetlands was one tiny fragment spanning the Iran-Iraq border, a pathetic remnant of its former glory.

Partow and his team examined the images for weeks, using mathematical algorithms to classify each pixel as a specific type of land cover. They determined that over 90% of the former marshlands were now covered with dry mud, dead vegetation and thick salt crusts. Even the small surviving wetland in northern Hawizeh appeared anemic, on the verge of collapse.

The emotional impact of this knowledge set Partow on his task with a renewed sense of purpose, reasoning that UNEP could use this knowledge to gain international support to force Iraq to halt its drainage schemes. But before the destructive trend could be reversed, he needed to determine why these devastating changes to the marshlands had occurred. He focused on two possible culprits: upstream dams in Iraq, Syria, and Turkey, and Iraq's local drainage projects.

Partow easily obtained reliable data on the upstream dams and their effect on water flow into Iraq, but dependable descriptions of recent hydraulic modifications in southern Iraq proved more difficult to acquire. He realized that the official Iraqi reports of these projects were obviously propaganda, but could he place any more reliance on the reports of Iraqi refugees and opposition groups? Even humanitarian organizations such as AMAR Appeal—headed by Baroness Nicholson, a Member of the European Parliament who staunchly opposed Saddam Hussein—could be influenced by political motivations.

Realizing that any of the information he obtained could be suspect, Partow undertook the tedious task of cross-referencing every source, using his best judgment to sort fact from fiction. The satellite images clearly delineated the canals draining the marshes, and levees and ditches could be faintly discerned, but many of the major dams were difficult to detect because they had been hidden beneath existing bridges. Slowly and methodically, he developed a remarkably complete understanding of the massive engineering scheme undertaken by Iraq to drain the wetlands.

Partow's report, "The Mesopotamian Marshlands: Demise of an Ecosystem," created an enormous international outcry when it was released in May 2001. As expected, Iraq launched an aggressive attack against UNEP's findings, eventually issuing a rebuttal report. In addition, the government of Turkey harshly criticized the suggestion that its upstream dams had potentially impacted the environment of Iraq. The electronic version of the report circulated through the Iraqi expatriate community, passing from person to person via internet discussion boards and e-mail, eventually reaching my husband, Azzam Alwash.

THE BIRTH OF THE EDEN AGAIN PROJECT

Azzam had spent his childhood in the southern Iraqi town of Nasriya, and his father took him on many memorable trips through the idyllic marshlands during the 1960s. Leaving Iraq in 1975, Azzam attended university in California where we met and married. He often spoke to me of the marshlands and promised to someday take me there, but his hopes were dashed in 1991 with the failure of the Gulf War to free his country. To put his frustration to good use, Azzam became active in several expatriate groups working against the Iraqi government.

In 1994, Azzam and I attended the AMAR Appeal press conference in London releasing its report on the drying of the marshes. We were both devastated by the evidence of the rampant destruction that the world had allowed Saddam to achieve. The information focused Azzam's anger, and he began to take a more active role opposing the Ba'ath regime. The only way to save the marshes and his country, he decided, was to remove Saddam from power. Every night he worked at this daunting task, using the Internet to generate grass-roots support among other Iraqi expatriates, organizing demonstrations, and setting up conferences aimed at bringing the crimes of Saddam and his cronies to light.

In 1999, Azzam was invited to join the Board of Directors of the Iraq Foundation, a group founded by Iraqi expatriate intellectuals including Rend and Basil Rahim, Kanan Makiya, Barham Salih, Laith Kubba, and Ghassan Rassam. The foundation worked actively in support of human rights and democracy in Iraq, meeting regularly with U.S. government officials and organizing conferences and symposia, while at the same time providing humanitarian and social support to Iraqi refugees in the United States. This connection allowed him to expand his political activities, and he began using all his vacation days to fly across the country and even to Europe, lobbying government officials and joining in the various congresses and meetings of opposition groups.

When the UNEP report was released in 2001, the extent of

devastation that had been wreaked over a single decade stunned Azzam. As he examined the recent satellite image, he became overwhelmed by a visceral sense of despair. To his trained eyes, the image was as repugnant as a photograph of a dismembered body. The AMAR Appeal report had shown that about a third of the marshes had been dried during the early 1990s, but no hard evidence of further desiccation had been brought forth in the intervening years. No one, including Azzam, had realized that Saddam had achieved nearly total desiccation. In the back of his mind, he had always believed the marshlands were too large to be destroyed, too resilient to be annihilated so quickly.

Together we discussed the ramifications of this new data. For years he had been working with the Iraqi opposition, fighting Saddam with words, failing with those words to rescue any portion of the marshlands. The time for rhetoric had passed; immediate action was required to rescue the dying ecosystem. But what action could we realistically undertake to restore wetlands in Iraq? We debated and discarded the possibilities until late that night, when Azzam conceived a desperate plan: we could ask the United States military to bomb those dams and levees.

As he saw it, Coalition forces regularly targeted Iraqi military installations in retaliation for violations of the cease-fire agreement. Why not use one of those missions to blast some holes through those earthen levees that were holding water back from the marshlands? Even if the Iraqi government immediately repaired the damage, a temporary re-flooding of the dried marshlands would bring welcome relief to both the ecosystem and its people. The influx of fresh water would germinate the seeds aging in the dried mud, extending the window of opportunity for future restoration without requiring deliberate re-planting of the native vegetation. And the marsh dwellers, we thought, would see the re-flooding as an indication of support for their way of life, a beacon of hope in the dark night of their misery.

The Iraqi government had already exiled all civilians from the marshes, so we anticipated that a careful selection of targets should eliminate any danger to human lives. We hesitated to bring more violence to an area that had already suffered so much brutality, but in the end, we decided that potential military intervention represented the only viable short-term solution—but of course such action would have to be carefully planned by Coalition forces with better information than we possessed.

While we worked toward that mission, we also planned to simultaneously undertake a public education campaign to focus worldwide attention on the plight of the marshes and their people. Our ultimate goal would be to convince the Iraqi government to at least sustain the small surviving portion of the marshlands, thereby preserving a natural reservoir of its biological and cultural resources and retaining the possibility for a future restoration of the larger marshlands.

Azzam decided to present our case to the U.S. Department of State, but to convince them to ask for military action against Saddam's desiccation structures, we needed to develop data to prove our plan could succeed. Dedicating a corner of our suburban house to the project, we began spending all our evenings and weekends working on a study of the feasibility for environmental restoration through military bombardment.

First, we needed to know the exact locations of the drainage structures emplaced around the marshlands, and our best resource proved to be Azzam's father, Jawad. He had served as General Director of Irrigation for the governorate of Dhi Qar, in the heart of the marshlands, during the 1960s and went on to work in the central government ministry for 20 years, ending up as the General Director of Irrigation for the entire country. He knew the water distribution system in Iraq better than anyone else. That Thanksgiving, we cleared off the table early and rolled out classified maps (lent to Azzam from an employee of the National Security Council) for a real family feast of hydrologic data. Jawad patiently explained the details of Iraq's water delivery system, which includes tens of thousands of canals, some of them originally excavated by the ancient Sumerians.

We encountered greater difficulty in obtaining numerical data on present-day water flow through Iraq, since Saddam's government maintained that all hydraulic data was classified. I undertook the library research, unearthing extensive data on historical water flow through Iraq (dating from the Ottoman Empire) in the basements of the University of California library. Azzam devised a method to update the old data using more recent information on the inflows from Turkey and Syria and then calculated how much of the water could be spared for the marshlands.

One of Azzam's colleagues in the Iraqi opposition, Dr. Hassan Janabi, was working as a water resources engineer in Australia. Janabi was born in southern Iraq and—like Azzam—retained many fond memories of his trips to the marshlands as a boy. He was forced to flee Iraq as a young man after being arrested by Saddam's secret police and brutally tortured. Australia granted him political asylum, but he never forgot Iraq or the marshlands, and he wrote numerous articles publicizing their destruction. Janabi was eager to help. An expert in the management of water resources in arid environments, he reviewed Azzam's calculations, smoothed over some rough points, and fully concurred with the conclusion that adequate water supplies existed to sustain the Iraqi marshlands, if only the political will prevailed.

With the feasibility study completed, Azzam asked Rend Rahim of the Iraq Foundation to arrange a meeting with the State Department. With degrees from Cambridge and the Sorbonne, Rend possessed extraordinary intellectual and diplomatic skills and also an extensive list of personal and political contacts, which she placed at our disposal. Like us, she felt hesitant about the use of military intervention but decided that our concerns should be voiced in the hopes of developing a less drastic solution. She called Tom Warrick, who was at the time working as a special consultant at the State Department; he had authored the genocide indictment against Slobodan Milošević, and she knew that his dearest ambition was to write another against Saddam Hussein for his treatment of the Marsh Arabs of Iraq.

January 2002 found the three of us desperately late by the time we entered the State Department conference room and met twelve people patiently waiting, including not only key State Department staff but also representatives from the Environmental Protection Agency and the Central Intelligence Agency. Azzam fumbled with the computer projector while I passed around business cards, my hands shaking. Suddenly we felt foolish—a couple of insignificant citizens plotting military strategy for the world's superpower. But our passion for rescuing the marshlands was restored as the government officials displayed intense interest in our proposals and asked probing questions: the meeting lasted several hours.

Unfortunately our plan was ultimately denied, for three reasons. First, the State Department's water resources expert believed that the main reason for the desiccation of the marshlands was the infilling of the reservoirs behind the large dams of Turkey and Syria. Even if we managed to completely destroy the levees and dams in southern Iraq, he argued, the quantity of water flowing into Iraq was no longer sufficient to maintain the integrity of the wetland ecosystem. Second, the CIA's environmental expert believed that re-flooding the marshes could be counterproductive because satellite images suggested that the ground was encrusted with salt and probably saturated with dangerous pollutants; in his opinion, adding water would simply spread the salt and pollutants and worsen the problem. Finally, we were told that an AMAR Appeal survey of marsh dweller refugees in Iran had concluded that most of them wouldn't return to their natural environment even if the marshes were restored.

Although we returned to California feeling defeated, it was only shortly thereafter that Warrick—clearly eager for us to document Saddam's crimes against the marsh dwellers—called Rend and encouraged us to prepare a proposal to conduct a more comprehensive study of the restoration potential of the Iraqi marshlands. We developed a straightforward scope of work: 1) evaluate whether enough water currently flowed into southern Iraq to re-flood the marshlands; 2) determine whether re-flooding the marshlands would restore the ecosystem or engender further damage; and 3) explore the question of whether the marsh dwellers would return if the ecosystem were restored. We didn't want to simply re-do the work of the UNEP report. The devastation had been proven—we wanted to propose specific actions for remediation. Rend polished our rough plan and bundled it with the Iraq Foundation's annual proposal for its other humanitarian projects.

In July 2002, the project was finally approved, and Congress granted us $220,000. The formal title of the project was "Evaluation of the Restoration Potential of the Mesopotamian Marshlands," but we immediately coined the name "The Eden Again Project" and dove into the work.

IS THERE ENOUGH WATER TO RESTORE THE MARSHES?

We needed an expert engineering team to address the question of available water resources, and Issam Ali, an Iraqi-American civil engineer also involved in the anti-Saddam movement, agreed to take on the task. His consulting firm had just completed an engineering analysis of the Euphrates River in Turkey, so they were very familiar with the hydrology of the area. Ali would be responsible for compiling a Geographic Information Systems (GIS) model of southern Iraq that would enable us to pinpoint every hydraulic structure and to rapidly compare features from various time periods while envisioning restoration options.

We hired another engineering firm, Exponent, to develop a computer model that would use our limited water flow data to analyze how much of the marshlands could be re-flooded given various water flow conditions. A young Italian engineer at Exponent, Andrea Cattarossi, set to work developing an interactive tool to evaluate potential restoration scenarios.

Next we needed an ecological team to assess whether re-flooding would restore or harm the ecosystem, along with someone to manage the ecological aspects of the project, since we were both still working full-time at our paying jobs. We decided to use a large portion of our funding to hire a full-time biologist for one year. Unexpectedly, we encountered great difficulty in attracting a suitable candidate; by this time there were rumblings of another war with Iraq, and ecologists, generally pacifist by nature, recoiled from any project that could potentially be construed as supportive of the war effort. Finally, we convinced the talented Dr. Michelle Stevens to take a sabbatical from the California Department of Water Resources, where she had recently managed a major ecological restoration project for the San Joaquin and Sacramento Rivers. She courageously began work on a conceptual restoration plan for one of the largest and most devastated wetland ecosystems in the world—without ever setting foot on its ground—knowing full well that she would probably never see any results from this quixotic effort.

DO THE MARSH DWELLERS WANT TO RETURN?

To address the third question, we needed to interview marsh dwellers and evaluate their enthusiasm for returning to the marshlands. Those in the Iranian refugee camps had apparently already indicated their inclination to live in cities, preferably located in Europe or Australia. Rend recommended that we contact AMAR Appeal to learn more about their survey of those refugees. Dr. Peter Clark, their executive director, reiterated his opinion that marsh dwellers in the refugee camps had suffered too much to return to the hard life of the marshes. Many of the families comprised only women, children and old men, and he believed this demographic could not survive in the challenging natural environment without the support of robust adult males. The younger adult refugees had literally grown up in the camps and therefore lacked any of the necessary skills to make a living from the traditional activities of fishing, fowling, reed weaving, or buffalo herding. Based on his experience with these refugees, Dr. Clark questioned whether restoring the marshlands was a worthwhile endeavor.

"Probably the land would be better used for petroleum development or field agriculture," he told me. "No one really wants to live in a swamp." Disappointed in the results of this conversation, we had to reconsider the entire underpinnings of our project. Part of our desire for restoring the marshlands hinged on preserving its natural ecological and historical values, but our primary objective was to enable the marsh dwellers to return to their traditional way of life. Restoring the marshlands to preserve their biodiversity entailed a very different project from one that included families living within the restored environment. We obviously needed to research this question further.

Reaching again into the Iraqi expatriate community, we contacted Ramadan Badran, another of Azzam's colleagues. His family came from the marshes, and he knew of a large group of Iraqi refugees living in San Diego, many of whom hailed from the marshlands. This community had managed to maintain contact with their families back in Iraq, and he assured us that they would be eager to share their perspectives.

Badran set up a meeting with about a hundred Iraqis in San Diego. Azzam presented the results of our study so far, and a lengthy and lively discussion followed. Every person at the meeting favored restoring the marshlands; the need for their revival seemed so obvious that it apparently didn't even require discussion. Displaying an innate trust in the healing power of nature, the Iraqis were confident that simply adding water to the dried land would restore their treasured wetlands.

"The marshlands are like our Statue of Liberty of Iraq," one woman declared. "They are a symbol of our great heritage, a source of great pride to all Iraqis." But another woman suggested that attracting marsh dwellers would require more than just the return of the natural marshland ecosystem; they would also want medical clinics, schools, safe drinking water and food, access to markets, cell phones and Internet connections. The marsh dwellers wished to maintain their traditional lifestyle in the marshlands, but they also wanted the necessities and conveniences of modern life within their natural environment.

CAN THE MARSHLANDS BE RESTORED?

With our preliminary work underway, Michelle and I turned our attention to the centerpiece of the project—convening a conference of wetlands experts to examine the results of our study and judge the restoration potential of the Iraqi marshlands. Within a month, we assembled a comprehensive panel of world experts who agreed to take time from their hectic research and lecture schedules to help the Iraqi marshes; not one of them asked for a salary or even an honorarium, merely reimbursement for their travel expenses.

The panel included Dr. Edward Maltby, the author of AMAR Appeal's scientific study of the marshlands; Hassan Partow, the author of UNEP's report; Dr. Joy Zedler, a faculty member at both the University of Wisconsin and the University of California and the chair of the National Academy of Sciences' Committee on Wetlands; Dr. Curt Richardson, head of the Duke University Center for Wetlands; Dr. Tom Crisman, Director of the University of Florida's Center for Wetlands; Dr. Mary Kentula, one of the U.S. Environmental Protection Agency's top wetlands experts; Dr. Brian Coad, an expert on Iraqi fish, from the Canadian Museum of Nature; and Mike Evans, one of Birdlife International's experts on birds of Iraq and the only panel member who had actually ever been in the marshlands.

We commenced the workshop on February 16, 2003, just as major anti-war demonstrations began across the world. As the presentations and discussions progressed, the scientists overwhelmingly supported restoration of the Mesopotamian Marshlands, delineating numerous practical reasons why they should be recovered. The panel also expressed considerable optimism for the restoration potential of the marshlands.

"We can create wetlands out of desert," said Dr. Curt Richardson. "This situation is much easier: marshlands have survived here for millennia, meaning that the soil properties are optimal for wetland habitat. Roots and seeds are most likely still present, and if water can be re-introduced then the vegetation should quickly reappear."

When the panel began to discuss the first steps of the restoration process, we worried that these university professors would design a multi-million dollar research project that would delay actual restoration actions for years to come. Instead, they recommended rapid implementation of pilot projects, suggesting that a few small areas of the dried marshes could be initially re-flooded and the results closely monitored. If the outcome seemed positive, the pilot project should be expanded to re-flood larger areas. It could be that easy.

THE IRAQ WAR AND THE UNHOLY SCRAMBLE FOR MONEY

A month later, Coalition forces invaded Iraq. We watched TV almost continuously, scanning the background landscape for signs of the dried marsh. While the war unfolded before us, we recognized the possibility that the pilot projects outlined by our blue-ribbon panel could actually be implemented. We rapidly evolved a new plan: instead of lobbying from afar, Azzam would go to Iraq and work on restoring the marshlands with the local people who had remained.

At that critical moment, however, Eden Again's funding disappeared. We had completed the scope of work and spent the money from the State Department grant when they informed us that the funding would not be renewed. Our project had been financed by the Iraq Liberation Act, and now that Iraq had been freed, all the money earmarked for that purpose would move back to the General Fund.

Disappointed but not discouraged, we pursued private sources of funding. I was adept at preparing winning grant proposals, and we assumed that private foundations would be eager to aid such an intriguing project. But our best efforts failed; even with the assistance of a professional grant writer, our proposals were rejected by a dozen wealthy foundations that specialized in supporting international environmental work. We gradually realized that we had been stymied by the requirements of the Patriot Act, which in its efforts to deny funding to terrorist groups had also had a chilling effect on grants to any organization working in the Middle East.

We were heartened in April 2003 when the U.S. Agency for International Development (USAID), announced $1.7 billion in funding for the reconstruction of Iraq. Washington gossip held that the funding would be divided amongst seven to eight huge contracts, and marshland restoration would be included in the contract for agricultural reconstruction. Shortly thereafter, Peter Reiss of Development Alternatives International (DAI) contacted us. He assured us that USAID would contract with DAI to implement restoration of agriculture in Iraq. To our great delight, Reiss told us that he managed an existing USAID project under an "Indefinite Quantity Contract," meaning that new tasks could be added as needed and there was no limit to the amount of money that could be spent. We asked if he could use this existing contract to fund an initial expedition to the marshes, including the Eden Again team and some members of our scientific panel, and he quickly agreed. Azzam cleared his schedule for May 15.

But Reiss kept citing bureaucratic delays in arranging the expedition, so in late May we went to Geneva instead, where UNEP was hosting a Mesopotamian Marshlands Roundtable Discussion. Michelle had set up a series of pre-meeting interviews with each of the major international conservation groups based in Geneva— Wetlands International, the Ramsar Secretariat, World Wildlife Fund, and the International Conservation Union (IUCN)—but each of the organizations shied away from working with us, implying that they would not operate in Iraq until the American-led occupation was over. It was clear that they saw our project as American, not Iraqi, and they wanted nothing to do with Americans at that time.

All of these groups attended the roundtable meeting the next day, along with Hassan Partow, representatives from USAID, the U.S. Department of State, the UN's Food and Agriculture Organization (FAO), the World Health Organization, Birdlife International, a few university professors including Dr. Maltby, and of course the Baroness. We were excited to finally meet Derek Scott and Richard Porter, the world's leading experts on birds and wildlife of Iraq's marshes; they spoke eagerly of connecting with Azzam in Iraq for their planned expedition in September 2003. But eventually the meeting degenerated into a series of power plays; apparently we weren't the only group looking for funding.

The Baroness came bearing letters from five local sheikhs, all apparently asking her to act as their representative. With those affirmations in hand, she proposed that AMAR Appeal be selected as coordinator of all reconstruction activities in the marshlands.

The USAID team made it equally clear that they wanted to take charge. They informed the group that they would lead the initial expedition because the U.S. controlled military access on the ground. They welcomed other interested parties to join them on later expeditions. The State Department representative made the enigmatic statement that they "wanted to reduce everyone's expectations for marshland restoration."

The UN organizations watched the other parties with complacency; it was clear that UNEP anticipated that they would be in charge of the restoration project, and that all other parties would coordinate under their umbrella.

The Italian Ministry of Environment, Land and Sea (IMELS)[7] was represented at the meeting by Augusto Pretner. Italian troops were providing security for the governorate of Dhi Qar in the heartland of the marshlands, he said, and IMELS was interested in helping the local people recover their lost heritage. He told us of his strong personal interest in the marshlands because of their resemblance to his own

---

[7]   The Ministry at the time was known as the Ministry of Environment and Territory; to avoid confusion, we have utilized its current designation throughout the book.

beloved Venetian Lagoon. Augusto is one of Italy's foremost experts in water resources, and he knew that IMELS's experience with restoring and protecting this historic wetland could be useful to Iraq.

He questioned us thoroughly about the Eden Again project, and then encouraged us, along with others at the meeting, to submit a proposal to IMELS for developing a plan to restore the Iraqi marshlands.

Meanwhile in Iraq, restoration efforts were already underway.

5. BLESSED FLOOD

[In 629 AD] the waters of the Tigris and Euphrates rose to a height never reached before or since, causing many great breaches. [The Persian governor] made special efforts to stop the breaches, but the water had the better of him … [he] rode out in person to block the breaches, he scattered money right and left; he … crucified on certain breaches 40 dam builders in one day, but all that was of no avail against the force of this water. With the advent of the Arabs into Iraq, the Persians were kept too busy fighting, consequently the Bata'ih [medieval Arabic term for the marshlands] was made wider and more extensive.

—al-Baladhuri (ca. 850 AD) Origins of the Islamic State

In March 2003, Ali Shaheen still served as the Director of Irrigation for the governorate of Dhi Qar. As Coalition troops entered Iraq, the province's military governor fled and Shaheen quietly celebrated the ignominious retreat of this man who had imprisoned him for simply requesting a supply of drinkable water to villages around the dried marshes. Shaheen stayed at his office in Nasriya as Iraqi and Coalition troops battled for control of the bridges crossing the Euphrates River and the Saddam River (also known as the Main Outfall Drain). Shaheen watched his rivers and contemplated a long-desired action—returning water to the marshlands of his youth. But he waited, because he remembered the abandonment of southern Iraq in 1991, and he still doubted the Coalition's resolve to finally remove Saddam Hussein from office.

As the war progressed, Shaheen watched his rivers enlarge. The fall of Saddam's government coincided with the spring floods: with no one governing the rivers, huge quantities of water were streaming southward into his district. By April, there was still no central control over the system and the Gharraf River began overflowing onto adjacent lands. Lives were at risk, but there was no government to give Shaheen instructions, no central authority to grant him permission to act. The only way to alleviate the floodwaters was to open the Bedaa Regulator on the Gharraf, but opening the regulator was literally a capital crime because it could release water into the dried marshes. If Shaheen opened the floodgates and the Ba'ath government returned, he would be executed and his family would suffer severe consequences. A quiet and unassuming man and the father of six young children, Shaheen knew that he should do what every other General Director in the ministry was doing: wait for instructions from the new government.

Shaheen opened the regulator.

The Bedaa Regulator controls the flow of water from the Gharraf into agricultural areas and also downstream into the Abu Zirig marsh on the southwest corner of the Central Marshes. The gate had been closed for more than a decade and a thick deposit of silt had accumulated on the upstream side, so it had to be opened slowly and gradually so that the water flowed fast and carved out the deposited silts. As Shaheen opened the sluice gates, his trepidation turned to delight with the cascading water. Finally he could save his river and his regulator; finally he could simply do his job. As water gushed through the dry channel, a spontaneous celebration erupted in the community gathered on the riverbanks. Young men fired rifles in the air and old men cried: Shaheen had brought life back to his home town of Islah.

He returned to his office and waited for the security police to come and arrest him. But the dreaded retribution never arrived. He went back to Abu Zirig and observed that a huge lake was accumulating behind the earthen embankments that had been emplaced to block water from entering the marshes. The local people asked if he could remove the embankments and allow water to flow back into the marshlands. Feeling courageous, Shaheen requisitioned a few backhoes and ordered them to breach the embankments. All they had to do was dig out a small hole, then the water flowing through, faster and faster, carved out a massive break in the dyke. The water streamed over the dry land, soaking the crusted soil and gradually drifting outwards, expanding into a broad glistening lake.

Like a man gone mad, Shaheen spent the next few days with the backhoes, ordering breach after breach, re-flooding several areas within the former Central Marshes. Aquatic life streamed in along with the water. Thousands of fish wiggled through the breaches and gradually transformed from river-green to marsh-brown as they acclimated to their ancient homes. A fleet of *mashuf* appeared from nowhere and within days dozens of fishermen delightedly plied the fresh waters, their joyful voices ringing over the bright waves, happy to taste again the succulent catch, thankful for the means to once again earn a living. Robyn Dixon of the Los Angeles Times was the first journalist to witness the miracle, and he wrote on May 5, 2003:

> "Fuhud, Iraq—Khoor Alaa Bedar sat in the bottom of a flat wooden boat and heard the music of water lapping at its sides ... as [he] crossed a lake that just a few weeks ago wasn't there. A melody of contentment played in his heart. Eleven years of trying to be something he could not were over for Bedar, 30. Every generation in family memory had been fishermen, and trying to eke out a living as a farm worker on a dusty, dried-up plateau had never felt right. Now he [was] a fisherman again. ... 'We knew Saddam was closing off the water,' Bedar said, "and when he ran away the water came back.'"

Shaheen ran into trouble when he tried to re-flood the Ghamuga marsh. The former governor had given the lands of this dried marsh to Ba'ath party members who were still loyal to Saddam, and they refused to allow Shaheen to breach the embankment holding water back from the dried marsh, even though the parched earth had never been put into productive use. By this time, Italian troops had taken charge of Dhi Qar, so he returned with a platoon of Italian soldiers, but even they could not convince the purported land owner to acquiesce. He left that problem for the future government to solve and turned his attention to the Hammar Marshes.

The Hammar Marshes were fed by water from the Euphrates River, and like the Gharraf, opening their regulators had been forbidden by penalty of death for many years. Shaheen reasoned that if the Ba'ath government returned to power, he was already a dead man: he might as well be a dead man several times over, so he decided to open the regulators on the Euphrates. A ceremony seemed appropriate, and he invited some local dignitaries to witness the event, including a group of U.S. Marines who had been assisting the local government. Their leader, Major Robert Carr, was a tough guy, but as the water spread over the dry land, tears began to stream down his face. The locals were so touched by this unexpected display of emotion that they spontaneously brought Major Carr gifts as a remembrance of the occasion so that he would never forget their appreciation for his team's work.

THE FIRST SCIENTIFIC EXPEDITION TO THE MARSHLANDS

"You won't believe it, Suzie—there's water as far as the eye could see, a huge lake that wasn't there a month ago—I swear to you the local people here are already re-flooding the marshes!" Azzam was so excited I could hardly understand what he was saying. He was calling me from the roof of his hotel in downtown Basra via a USAID satellite phone and the connection was terrible. It was his first night back in Iraq after a 25-year exodus and he was trying to share the experience with me on the other side of the globe. I was thrilled that he was so happy, yet bitterly disappointed not to be by his side; but our daughter Hannah was only 10 and Norah only 8 years old and so we had decided that it would be foolhardy for both of us to go into the war zone. Even Azzam, wary of ongoing gun battles and the profusion of land mines in the marshlands, had waited until the official USAID expedition had been arranged.

The trip, initially planned for May, had been delayed and scaled back. Finally the expedition began in early June and included Douglas Pool, an environmental expert from USAID, Duke University's Dr. Curt Richardson who had served on the Eden Again scientific panel, Reiss and Azzam. They flew together into Kuwait, and after a couple of nights in the luxurious USAID compound, the team loaded their gear into a hired car and joined a seemingly endless convoy of military tanks and materiel headed into Iraq.

At the border, Reiss insisted that everyone don flak jackets and helmets in the 130° heat. When they reached Basra, the shiny skyscrapers of Kuwait seemed a thousand miles away as the group wound their way through bomb-cratered streets lined with burned-out buildings. Azzam had anticipated being overcome by a wave of nostalgia, but in Basra he felt as out of place as the Americans. He discarded the flak jacket.

First the team had to complete a course on land mine safety at the British compound, and then they checked into Basra's finest accommodation. Azzam found lice on the bed, lizards on the wall and mold in the shower. He decided to wait in the lobby for the rest of the team to get settled.

A tall, thin man entered and asked for Azzam Alwash; he spoke in an Iraqi accent but wore the jeans and casual sports jacket of a foreigner. It was Hassan Janabi, the Iraqi-Australian civil engineer who had been instrumental in reviewing the Eden Again hydrological studies.

Azzam and Janabi had initially become acquainted via the Internet, working together to develop plans for post-war reconstruction of Iraq. In February 2003, Janabi had accepted a job with the Coalition's Office of Humanitarian and Reconstruction Activities (ORHA), in a position funded by the Australian Overseas Aid Agency (AusAID). He had already spent several months in Iraq as an advisor to the Ministry of Irrigation —now known as the Ministry of Water Resources— working alongside Azzam's father, Jawad, who had also returned to help reconstruct his homeland.

Janabi and Azzam were deep in conversation when Ramadan Badran, our connection to the marsh dweller refugees in San Diego, stepped into the hotel lobby. True to his word, he had sold his trucking business in California as soon as the war began and moved his family back to Iraq, once again living on the fringes of his beloved marshlands. Badran was also working for ORHA with the British who were leading the Coalition forces in the south, serving as liaison officer to help build local councils that would hopefully run the Iraqis' affairs in a democratic manner. But his heart was with the marshlands project and he tagged along, eager to be a part of the team.

The whole experience began to take on the quality of a surreal Hollywood homecoming as the group went to lunch and found Baroness Nicholson already seated at the restaurant, a silk scarf demurely tied beneath her chin. Azzam felt more grounded when the waiter brought in a huge platter of *zobaidy* (a variety of pomfret), fresh caught from the Gulf, and one of the tastiest dishes in the world.

RE-FLOODING IN EAST HAMMAR MARSH

It was late afternoon by the time lunch was over, but Azzam couldn't wait to get out to the marshland, so the whole crowd travelled to the waterfront, boarded two wooden motorboats and headed northwest towards the marshes. The canal they travelled on had never been dried; dense reeds and date palms lined either side of the canal, growing just as lush and verdant as Azzam remembered them. At the river's edge, women cut reeds in the fading sun, their bodies draped with the black robes called *abaya*, forming the triangular silhouette that was such a familiar sight to Azzam.

Historically, this canal connected the southeastern end of Hammar Marsh with the Gulf. For a part of each day, water from the Euphrates flowed down from the marsh through this canal into the ocean. But the Gulf is home to huge tidal forces, and as the tide rose it reversed the canal's flow, forcing water back up into the marshes. When Saddam undertook the drying of the marshes, a large earthen dam had to be built across the canal to keep the rising tides from forcing water upstream and re-flooding the marshes every day.

As the boats sped through the waterway, this dam came into view, apparently blocking further progress. But as they drew near, Azzam could see a breach in the embankment spanning about 50 feet (15 m) across. A group of men stood on the banks of the canal near the breach, and Azzam asked the boatman to pull up to them so they could talk. The men belonged to a tribe of marsh dwellers originally from this area known as Garmat Ali. They related to the team that the military governor of Basra had fled when Coalition troops entered the province. Seizing this opportunity, their tribe borrowed a front-end loader from a local contractor and dug a small ditch through the embankment down to the water line, then the flow of the water through the ditch eroded the embankment further as the incoming tide pushed the water back into the marshes, thus creating this huge breach that allowed water to re-flood the marshes of Garmat Ali. It had been so simple.

Two friends of the boat driver joined them as they were talking; they had lived in the marshes of Garmat Ali before they had been dried, and they asked to accompany the team past the breach. Barred from the area for many years, they were anxious to learn what had become of their ancestral home. Reiss and Nicholson had some concerns about security, but finally the men boarded the boats and the team motored through the breach and stopped.

A refreshing evening breeze ruffled over the group as they sat awestruck by the scene. Water the color of milky weak tea lapped against the edges of the embankment and extended all the way out to the horizon. Just a few weeks before, this area had been barren desert: now there was a lake that covered over 50 square miles (130 km^2). Azzam marveled at the accomplishment of one day's work, astonished at the quantity of water that had been pushed into the basin by the tides. Peering over the side of the boat, he couldn't see the bottom through the silt-laden water, so he asked the boatman to test the depth with his pole. In most places it was about six feet (2 m), but some areas were deeper than the ten feet (3 m).

Of course the lake lacked vegetation: no reeds sprouted on its shores, no algae waved from its depths, not even duckweed dotted its surface. No birds fluttered overhead, no insects buzzed, no frogs croaked. The only sign of life was an occasional swish of a fish breaking

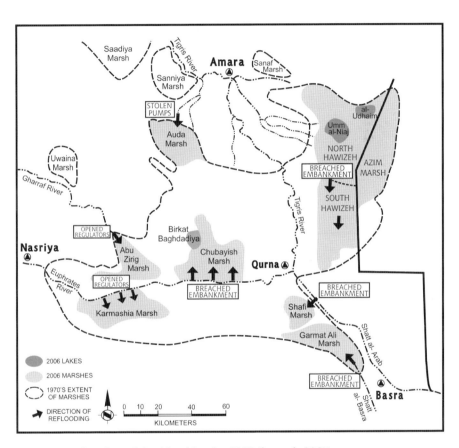

Figure 5. Reflooding of the Marshlands, 2003 through 2007

the water's surface. The barren lake worried Azzam. He recalled the dismal predictions of the CIA's environmental expert that nothing would grow even if the marshes were re-flooded. Had the efforts of the marsh dwellers simply created a lifeless pool of water?

The group forged their way further into the lake, puttering along for another hour without reaching the end of the flooded region. Suddenly the two marsh dwellers excitedly asked the boatman to veer north. Approaching the area they had indicated, the group could see a broad mound rising out of the water. Scattered over the mound they could see stumps of palm trees and foundations of destroyed mud huts. One of the men began to weep as he recognized his former village, once again overcome by grief at his loss. He lamented the fate of his people, born to be free in the marshes but forced by Saddam into urban beggary. Azzam was deeply moved by the man's sorrow but was also secretly satisfied that his emotional outburst demonstrated to the USAID team how much these people wanted their marshes back.

The boats turned back, gliding across the miraculous lake under a persimmon-and-pomegranate sky. When they returned to the breached embankment, a different group of men beckoned them. They too wanted to discuss the status of their former village in the marshlands. At this point in time, their clan was still weighing the benefits and drawbacks of leaving their new homes and returning to reclaim their ancestral land. They stated that thousands of families had been forcibly removed from this area of the marshes, and that all of them all come back if possible. But what they really needed to come back—in addition to water—were basic services: electricity, health care, schools, and access to markets.

OVERFLIGHT OF THE DRIED MARSHLANDS

The benefit of working with USAID became clear the next day, as a bright summer's dawn found the team boarding a massive military helicopter. Due to minefields and other residue of the wars fought in the marshes, an aerial view was the only way to survey the more inaccessible areas of the marshes, and so the British Royal Marines had agreed to let the team accompany them on their regular run from Basra to Amara so that the scientists could more fully assess the situation of the vast dried marshland

Azzam grabbed a jump seat near the window and waited while the pilot decided whether they could take off. Apparently the giant airships cannot operate at temperatures above 122°F, (50°C) and even at this early hour, it was already blazingly hot. But finally the rotors started and they rose in tight loops, staying within the protected airspace until they reached an altitude where they were no longer vulnerable to mortars launched from insurgents on the ground.

Nervously peering out the open back gate, Azzam could see the enormous gas flares streaming a hundred feet (30 m) high over the supergiant Rumaila oilfield. Moat-like canals with salt-encrusted banks bordered the northern edge of the oilfield, the side facing Iran. The surrounding landscape shimmered, a barren moonscape scattered with desert shrubs touched in cinnabar and ochre.

They flew north, passing over the wide, muddy waters of the Euphrates. A few meager groves of date palms dotted its riverbanks, faint reminders of the dense stands that remained vividly in Azzam's memory. The trees were also victims of Saddam's revenge on the south. Barren land stretched beneath them as far as the eye could see: the dried marshes.

Then the Glory Canal rose into view. Constructed by Saddam in the early 1990s to drain the Central Marshes, this mile-wide (1.6 km) moat collected the flow from the distributaries of the Tigris inland delta, diverting the water away from the marshes and dumping it into the Euphrates. Within two years of its completion, this structure had desiccated more than 700 square miles (1,800 km²) of wetlands. Even from this high altitude, Azzam was amazed at the size of the canal that stretched for 50 miles (80 km) across the dried landscape.

Saddam had claimed that the project was intended to irrigate agricultural fields in what he called the "reclaimed" marshlands. During the 1990s, heated debates had ensued between those who believed this story and those who knew it to be a lie. But as they flew over the vast expanse of empty dirt, Azzam took no gratification from knowing he had been correct. Instead of the lush fields of wheat and barley promised by the dictator, there was only desolate wasteland. A lone tractor sitting abandoned in a salt-dusted field testified to the agricultural uselessness of the land. The complete inhumanity of this act staggered the imagination, yet Azzam forced himself to look toward the future, not back on the past. The Glory Canal was full of water and he began to mentally design how to redirect that precious flow back into the marshlands.

The helicopter stopped at Amara and then lifted again and headed over what should have been uninterrupted desert, but suddenly Azzam spotted a huge lake of clear shallow water that wasn't supposed to be there. Checking the maps he had brought along, he determined that the lake covered a seasonal marsh known as Sanaf. No water had been seen on the satellite images of this area for the last ten years. The origin of this lake was a mystery.

As the helicopter turned south, the team gathered around the windows on the left side of the helicopter as a vast expanse of green appeared out of the desert dust: Hawizeh Marsh. A year ago, these wetlands stood as the last forlorn remnant of the entire Mesopotamian Marshlands. Saddam had never tried to completely drain the northern portion of Hawizeh because it spanned the border with Iran and served as a deterrent to invading forces. Although now it only covered about 250 square miles (650 km^2), from the air it shone like a sea of emerald green stranded within the brown desert sand, with several aquamarine lakes nestling like gems within its reeds. The team eagerly decided to investigate the area on the ground.

HAWIZEH AND SANAF MARSHES

It took about three hours to drive from Basra to Sanaf the next day. Hassan Janabi and two engineers from the Ministry of Water Resources, Jassim Asadi and Samira Shabeeb, accompanied the team, explaining the origin of this new lake. Apparently, the depression serves as a flood control basin for the release of excess water during high flows. In the spring of 2003, melting snow in the Taurus and Zagros mountains released huge amounts of water that naturally flowed into the depression called Sanaf, thus creating this seasonal water body.

On the ground, the team was stunned to see so much water: the clear blue lake, dizzying in the simmering desert sun, blended into the far-off horizon. As with the re-flooded Garmat Ali marsh, nothing much was growing in the lake, and only salt-tolerant desert flora such as tamarisk, saltbush, and glasswort surrounded its borders. Dr. Richardson sent the driver wading out into the lake to collect water and soil samples. His initial measurements indicated that the water was too salty to support freshwater aquatic life. He told Azzam not to expect the rebirth of a marsh here. Without a continuous influx of water, by late summer only mud cracks and salt crusts would remain.

The team then drove along the Musharra Canal toward Hawizeh Marsh, passing by families living in clusters of mud-brick huts, eking a living out of grazing emaciated cattle and collecting government rations. Although there was plenty of water in the canal, none of it was benefiting the surrounding land. The team could see no sign of the marshlands, but Azzam was encouraged by the substantial flow of water down the canal towards Hawizeh. Stopping to inspect a regulator on the canal, he noticed small turtles clambering to swim past the gates—a heartening indication of good water quality but a poignant illustration of wildlife trapped inside this man-made system.

Finally they drove up onto a steep embankment and Azzam was stunned by the vista before him: the desert ended abruptly in marshlands. He jumped from the car and laughed aloud as the vibrant green, verdant lushness filled his eyes and heart. The heat seared into him and the humidity had suddenly increased a hundredfold, but he didn't care: he felt as if he had passed from hell to heaven. Standing on the embankment, he looked west and saw nothing but desert; looking east, he saw nothing but marshland. Dense stands of reeds towered twelve feet (3.5 m) high, growing right up to the side of the embankment.

Dozens of *mashuf* were drawn up on the muddy shoreline beneath him. His spirits rose as he saw fishermen proudly offloading their catch, then maneuvering their slim canoes back through the rushes to net some more. The poles splashing into the water, mingled with the boatmen's convivial shouts, were a symphony to Azzam's ears. The dank vegetal smell, the stink of the fish, the smoke of a nearby fire filled him with nostalgia so sweet he felt transported to his youth.

He spoke at length to the men, trying to remember the Arabic names for the wildlife of the area. They were catching good-sized carp, a species introduced to the marshes, but the fishermen told him that native fish such as *bunni* and *gattan* still swam between the reeds. Further in the marshes, they told him, turtles abounded amidst the deafening croaks of frogs while otters rippled through the calm water. Deeper still into the reed jungle, large flocks of birds still paused in their migration and established nesting colonies.

From an ecological perspective, the importance of Hawizeh lay in its role as a sanctuary for the remaining wildlife of the marshlands. If the dried marshes could be restored, then Hawizeh would serve as their biodiversity bank. If ecological connections could be established between Hawizeh and any newly-restored marshes, then many of the species could naturally migrate back; if not, it may prove necessary to deliberately capture and transport animals to the other restored marshlands. Azzam's head swam with the possibilities, but these were questions to resolve in the future. For now, he felt satisfied that a decent reservoir of biodiversity remained. The sun was setting and the team needed to be back in Basra before dark when the insurgent *fedayeen* took control of the territory.

CHUBAYISH AND THE CENTRAL MARSHES

The next day, Azzam insisted on visiting the Central and Hammar Marshes, so the team took the fast road from Basra to Nasriya, rolling across a seemingly endless desert. After a while, Azzam asked the convoy to stop for a reconnaissance. Leaving the air-conditioned vehicle, the intense heat and dust clogged his lungs and for a few minutes he could hardly breathe. From a distance, the area had resembled the rest of the dry shrubby desert, but when he looked more closely at the landscape, he suddenly realized that they were actually in the dried marshlands. Kneeling down, he could see clear evidence of the former marsh— enormous mud cracks covered the ground, and within the soil he could discern bits of dried reeds along with small shells of snails and clams.

Large patches of soil were colored burnt orange and when he picked up some clods he discovered they were as hard and flinty as ceramic. Jassim came to his side and explained that after the marshes were dried, the reeds had been set on fire; in some cases the fires had burned down into the roots and smoldered for months, transforming the soil into red glass in the unnatural underground kiln.

Looking around, Azzam noticed the faint remains of a group of mud huts. Jassim pointed out the stumps of palm trees.

"They not only cut the date palms down," he said, "They pulled them up by the roots. Saddam's army purposely destroyed millions of trees. You see that low swale over there?" he continued. "That was a small channel; the locals would herd their water buffalo in a line over the same spot, so that their weight would compress the mud and make an opening so that the boatmen could pass through the reeds. That depression over there in the distance was a small pond. It looks white because it's covered with empty, sun-bleached snail shells."

Azzam was relieved to discover the meaning of the soil coloration. We had spent the last year poring over satellite images, wondering why the soils were red, and imagining that the white surfaces of the dried lakes were salt crusts: some scientists had predicted encrustations up to a foot (30 cm) thick. Re-flooding salt-encrusted land would create a catastrophe, but snail shells posed no such threat to the environment.

Back in the armored SUV, Azzam asked Jassim why he knew so much about the marshes.

"I am from Chubayish," he replied. "My whole life was in the marshes, as a child I went there every day to cut reeds and fish: I only left to go to university. Whatever you want to know about the marshes, I can tell you—let me take you to my hometown to meet my family."

Azzam remembered his childhood visits to Chubayish with his father with great clarity and fondness, and he had eagerly anticipated his return to the "Venice of Iraq" for months. Perhaps Jassim had been one of the young boys he had admired, paddling around on his own *mashuf*. But when they arrived at the town it was not at all the place that he remembered. In the old days, Chubayish was completely surrounded by marshes, accessible only by boat. The village was composed of more than 1500 islands, each covered with date palms, fruit trees and flower gardens; canals separated each island, and neighbors paddled canoes to visit each other. But after the marshes had dried there was no water for the canals, so the government had filled them with dirt to form narrow dusty streets that wound crookedly between nondescript cement block houses.

Deeply disappointed, Azzam followed Jassim to an ancient *mudhif* listing dangerously to one side like a sinking ship. The air was at least twenty degrees cooler inside the dark reed building due to breezes blowing through its lattice-work walls. Jassim's uncle greeted them, a wizened elderly man wearing a western-style business jacket over his traditional *dishdasha*, his head covered with the ubiquitous black-and-white checkered tribal cloth. Abu Abbas' face bespoke years of struggle, but his eyes were full of vitality and intelligence. Azzam explained who was on the team and what they were trying to accomplish.

Their host seated his guests against the reed walls on colorful rugs covering the dirt floor. By now, dozens of men had congregated inside, chattering excitedly and staring at the Americans while smoking endless cigarettes. Boys hurried through with brass trays carrying small glasses of hot tea. Azzam once again tasted the bitter brew that even the copious amounts of added sugar could not mitigate. The warm hospitality began to ease his disappointment with the town: at least the *mudhif* culture still flourished.

Abu Abbas emphatically thanked the Americans for liberating Iraq from Saddam.

"Our village used to be 60,000 people, but after the marshes dried we became less than 10,000. No one can live here without the marshes," he said. "You have to help bring them back: we cannot do it by ourselves." He spoke of water as the blood of the marshes; without it, the marshes and the lives of the people could not revive. To him, restoration of the marshes was a right of justice. He was so forceful that he left no doubt that these people wanted their marshes back.

Feeling guilty for not being able to stay at the *mudhif* for dinner, Azzam drove with the team to Nasriya. Azzam hadn't seen his hometown since 1970, and like Chubayish, it came as a terrible shock. Nasriya had always been a sleepy backwater town, he recalled, but in his youth, people took pride in what little they had. Streets were swept and washed daily, buildings were painted, and gardens were filled with trees and flowers. Now everything was ramshackle, grimy and rancid, full of jerry-rigged electrical wires, bombed houses, and garbage: the smell of raw sewage was nearly unbearable.

Azzam wanted numerical data on stream flow through the rivers and canals of Dhi Qar, so that he could quantify the amount of water available for restoration. He knew just who to ask—the Director General in the local office of the Ministry of Irrigation. That had been his father's job title when Azzam was a child, and now he was introduced to Ali Shaheen. Azzam eagerly inquired about the re-flooding of marshes in this area, but Shaheen replied in vague terms, darting nervous glances at all the strangers present. Azzam understood: his actions had not been authorized by Baghdad, and Shaheen remained fearful of repercussions now that the central government had regained control. Saddam's removal did not automatically transform the traditional command mentality of the ministry; Azzam would have to wait for a private interview to hear the complete story.

BACK TO BAGHDAD

Their field work concluded, the team drove up to Baghdad to present their preliminary findings to the Coalition Provisional Authority (CPA), where Azzam had an emotional reunion with his father. When the war began in 2003, the elderly Jawad had immediately volunteered to serve his adopted country; he didn't divulge that he had recently undergone a quadruple heart bypass. The Pentagon sent him to boot camp in Texas, issued him a colonel's commission and a gas mask and airlifted him into Baghdad, where he helped re-organize his former Ministry of Irrigation and purge it of Saddam's Ba'ath cronies. After a month, the heat and air pollution had proven too much for his weakened condition;

he was only holding on until Azzam could get to Baghdad to take his place. But before he would leave, Jawad insisted that he take Azzam to the Ministry of Water Resources so he could introduce him to the people who held the power of life and death over the marshlands.

At the ministry, Azzam and Hassan Janabi compared their observations and shared ideas for restoring their beloved ecosystem, vowing to work together to make their dreams a reality. Janabi intended to work through the central government: his goal was to form a center for restoration of the marshlands within the Ministry of Water Resources. Azzam aspired to form a non-profit environmental organization that would operate outside governmental control. Working together, they felt they would be unstoppable.

Reiss asked Azzam to present their results to the CPA staff, and about 50 people showed up, lured by Janabi's previous presentations. When the main electrical grid predictably failed, the presentation continued on batteries as everyone huddled around Azzam's laptop. His enthusiasm proved infectious and the USAID team was asked to return in July to conduct a more focused survey with an expanded scientific team.

Azzam and his father hired a driver to take them through the western desert to his sister's home in Jordan. He called me from Amman and we talked for awhile about the scenes of devastation he had witnessed. The task ahead seemed daunting. Dr. Richardson had expressed doubts whether natural marsh vegetation would re-sprout in the re-flooded marshes. He feared that the salty soil would inhibit the growth of reeds and freshwater plants. Problems could also result from oxidized organic material in the peaty soil; re-wetting could potentially create sulfuric acid, and plant growth would be stymied by the low pH. Dr. Richardson questioned whether a project of this magnitude could succeed, given the gross deterioration of the biological resources and the uncertainty of future water supplies. As one of the world's most prominent and optimistic authorities on wetland restoration, he advised Azzam to lower his expectations for restoration.

But the predictions of western scientists were not really important to us. What really mattered were the hopes and desires of the indigenous marsh dwellers. I asked Azzam whether he had obtained an answer to our most important question: did the marsh dwellers want their ecosystem restored? He answered with a poignant tale.

"A few days ago we were driving on a raised roadway through the dried marshes, surrounded on all sides by dusty, dry desert, not a drop of water in sight," he told me. "I noticed some activity to the side of the road and I asked the driver to stop. Below us on the parched earth was a family with all of their possessions laid out on the ground around them. They were marsh dwellers just returning from their forced exile in the north. The men were building a home: thick bundles of reeds had been placed into two lines of holes in the parched earth, and they were pulling the loose ends of the bundles together to form an arched support. On the ground next to them lay piles of reed mats to cover the arches and complete their home. These people were moving back into the dried marshlands with the simple expectation that the water would return and their ecosystem would be reborn. They returned purely on hope. If destitute, humiliated families like this could dare to hope for restoration, then I have to support them.

I agreed with Azzam. Neither of us knew what needed to be done to restore the marshes, or how many years of our lives it would take to accomplish the goal, but we had started down this road and were determined to continue.

6. INVENTING NATURE IRAQ

One day alone with young Shibil as he fished a lagoon, I said: 'Before I returned here, I thought I would never see the Marshes or any of you ever again. I thought you might all have vanished.' He slapped his bare chest with his hand, sending a sharp echo round the reed verge. 'Vanished? We, Madan? Do I look as if I would ever disappear?' He stood, laughing, in the prow of the canoe, brown and half-naked, his spear raised to strike down into the water. And I thought: 'No, of course you don't.'

—Gavin Young, Return to the Marshes (1977)

Before he returned home from Iraq, Azzam flew to Rome on a quest for funding that we both thought was unlikely to succeed. My efforts to raise money from private foundations had failed, and Peter Reiss had made it abundantly clear that we could expect little support from the USAID contract with DAI. We had been completely snubbed by the international conservation organizations. We even felt abandoned by the State Department. Everyone we had previously worked with seemed to have been re-assigned elsewhere, and the previously-enthusiastic Tom Warrick wouldn't return our phone calls anymore. The Eden Again project seemed doomed.

But at the Roundtable meeting in Geneva, the Italians had expressed interest in supporting marshland restoration, and Dr. Corrado Clini, the Director General[8] of the Ministry of Environment, Land and Sea (IMELS), had invited Azzam to meet with him in Rome, so to Rome Azzam travelled. Clini is a quintessential Italian— warmly gregarious yet innately urbane and sophisticated. Azzam's straightforward manner and infectious laugh sparked a spontaneous friendship between the two men. They passionately discussed the

---

[8] Dr. Clini became the Minister of IMELS in 2011.

situation in southern Iraq, especially the area of Italian influence in the governorate of Dhi Qar. Azzam described the unique ecosystem of the marshes and their ancient history, their destruction under the previous regime, and his dreams for their future restoration. Dr. Clini fully sympathized; Italy, he said, stood equally proud of its ancient culture and unique natural heritage and—amidst modernization and socioeconomic development projects—his ministry struggled to preserve both. Italian aid programs had assisted with ecological restoration projects in many other countries, and Dr. Clini offered the expertise of Italian engineers and scientists toward fulfilling Iraq's dreams of environmental reconstruction.

The next day, IMELS held a press conference and announced the initiation of a joint undertaking between Italy and the Iraq Foundation, to be known as the "New Eden Project." With tears in his eyes, Azzam draped a traditional gold-embroidered robe over Minister Altero Matteoli's shoulders and pronounced him an official Marsh Arab.

The promised Italian sponsorship should have energized Azzam, but he returned home and moped around the house for the rest of the summer, unsure of what the future held in store for him. The New Eden Project meant working in Iraq for long periods of time, and such a drastic change of plan does not come easily. The Italian aid bogged down in bureaucracy and we sometimes wondered if it would ever materialize. USAID postponed their July expedition indefinitely. Azzam yearned for action but lacked either resources or a plan.

Finally I pushed him out of the nest. My salary as a community college professor wasn't large but I figured that it would be adequate if we lived frugally. Planning that he would go to Iraq to initiate the project, hire a manager and return home to supervise the work from California, Azzam requested six months' leave from his employer. After working with the same company for 18 years, he assumed his partners would be glad to assist him in such an important project. Instead they summarily fired him and refused to honor their partnership agreement. Needless to say, the financial loss dampened Azzam's enthusiasm.

Two unexpected patrons came to our rescue: Robin and Nancy Wainwright. Robin had visited the marshlands while traveling through Iraq in the 1970s and fallen in love with the unique ecosystem. The deeply spiritual couple had been supporting peace initiatives in the Middle East for many years and had been following our project closely for several months. Just when our prospects were at their lowest ebb, these total strangers called and asked if we needed help. They ended up granting enough money to pay expenses for Azzam's first three months in Iraq, but it was their moral support that meant the most to us.

Their assistance helped Azzam overcome his inertia, and we started planning his trip in earnest. He needed field equipment, including a digital camera with a car charger, a state-of-the-art GPS unit, wading boots, desert boots, mosquito nets, a sleeping bag and water purification tablets. I insisted that he get a painful series of vaccinations and—because there was no medicine available in Iraq—managed to convince our family doctor to give him some full-spectrum antibiotics to combat cholera or whatever dread disease he might contract in the war zone.

Explaining his departure to our children broke Azzam's heart. Although we had tried to shield them from the death tolls on the nightly news, they knew Iraq was a very dangerous place and the possibility existed that he would not return from this "business trip." Azzam opened Gavin Young's book and once again showed them the photographs of the marsh dwellers.

"The people in these pictures are dying," he explained to them. "They're dying because Saddam Hussein destroyed the place where they lived. They need the marshlands restored and I want to help them put their lives back together."

He left on August 15, 2003, lugging two suitcases crammed with supplies and $10,000 cash in his pocket.

BAGHDAD WITHOUT A PLAN

Once in Baghdad, Azzam felt completely alone. He had no source of funding, no supporting organization, and no idea what to do next. He faltered momentarily and then called his childhood friend, Adel Rahoumi. An Iraqi-American like Azzam, Adel had also left behind his wife and children to help reconstruct his ancestral homeland. In New Jersey he had been an unappreciated artist and lackluster hotel caterer; in Baghdad he worked for the Coalition Provisional Authority (CPA) setting up town councils and bringing democracy to the Middle East.

He put Azzam up in the bedroom of his lean-to apartment

and recommended his cousin Zeid as Azzam's driver and general factotum. That night as the air conditioner turned on and off with the stop-and-start of electrical current, Azzam laid awake sweating and agonizing: "What in the world will I do tomorrow?"

If Zeid hadn't knocked on the door early the next morning, Azzam may well have stayed in bed and continued to wonder, but the need to keep his young assistant occupied spurred him into action. So they spent the next week driving around Baghdad. Every morning Azzam visited the Ministry of Water Resources (MoWR), introducing himself to the staff, drinking endless cups of bittersweet tea, and setting up an essential network of like-minded comrades. In the afternoon, he typically headed over to the nearby Presidential Palace to meet with staff of the CPA or to the Iraq Foundation office, where they had provided him with a desk. Evenings usually found him at an Internet café downloading e-mails. The CPA issued him a phone with a 914 area code so we spoke every night. Sometimes I could hear bombs exploding in the distance. I should have been worried, but somehow I had the feeling that my husband was invincible.

Azzam's most pressing need was data. He had to know how much water was available to restore the marshes and how it could be re-routed back to the ecosystem. He required precise information on the design parameters and locations of all water control structures in southern Iraq, including dams, weirs, barrages, and canals. But Azzam was a private citizen with no claim on this information, and Iraq was a country accustomed to guarding its water data like state secrets. Mentioning the marshlands worried some of the ministry staff who had been forced to engineer their destruction; they feared retribution, official or otherwise. But the name Jawad Alwash opened many doors, and Azzam gratefully realized that many within the ministry had a sincere desire to reverse the damage dictated by the former government.

No one advocated more forcefully for marshland restoration than Hassan Janabi. As a CPA advisor, he had already initiated the Center for Restoration of the Iraqi Marshlands (CRIM) within the MOWR. Azzam began working with Janabi, helping him create project sheets and briefing books. They invented the restoration plan as they went along, enjoying the freedom and camaraderie.

WITNESS TO A MIRACLE

But after a few weeks of Baghdad's insanity, Azzam craved the simplicity of the marshlands. Zeid refused to drive through the war zone, so Azzam rented a 1981 Chevy Malibu and convinced Janabi to assign an engineer to accompany him as an assistant. They stopped frequently at checkpoints—first those of the American military; then around Kut, where they passed through the Polish zone; then finally near Nasriya, where they saw the Italian soldiers with their black-feathered hats. Their first stop was the office of Ali Shaheen, who greeted Azzam warmly and assigned one of his employees as a local guide.

They were directed to Nasriya's best hotel, the Genoob, where it finally became clear to Azzam why the USAID team drove back to miserable accommodations in Basra every night—the lodgings here were even worse. The shower, fed directly from the river, dribbled oily brown water redolent of rotting fish. The bed sheets, never changed, reeked with the sweat of a hundred predecessors. But Azzam was too exhausted to care—at least there was air conditioning.

At dawn they headed east to the Hammar Marshes, driving along an embankment surrounded by rice farms, groves of palm and citrus trees, vegetable patches gleaming with ripe tomatoes and squash, and tank carcasses dating from the Iran-Iraq War. Weaving their way through a slow procession of dilapidated bicycles and horse-drawn carts, the three men stopped for hot cups of tea in the bustling town of Sug ash-Shuykh and then continued toward Garmat Bani Said, following one of the river distributaries that traditionally fed into the marshlands. Azzam recognized a water regulator on the river that had been built by his father. It had been recently opened and was allowing a small trickle of water into the marshlands. In the old days, this would have been the embarkation point where he and his father boarded a boat into the marshes, but now it was still mostly dry land.

They continued to drive along the elevated roadway. Finally they came to an area that the local engineer said had been re-flooded about five months previously. He called it Karmashia Marsh, but it didn't look much like a marsh, just a large expanse of shallow water that was essentially flooded desert. Anemic branches of tamarisk, the dominant shrub of the surrounding dry lands, were the only vegetation emerging from the water. The desert denizen was obviously struggling to survive in the waterlogged soil. Gnats and mosquitoes buzzed over the motionless water that sat steaming under the desert sun. Foamy balls of chartreuse algae clogged the shoreline where Azzam could see no sign of any reeds or rushes sprouting. He stepped into the dank lake to measure the water quality, but the readings weren't good—the salinity was very high and the oxygen content too low to even register on the meter.

Disheartened, the three engineers turned back to Nasriya. Azzam pondered the significance of the failure of marsh vegetation to re-sprout. The scientists of our Eden Again panel had suggested re-flooding small portions of the dried wetlands and monitoring the outcome. The local people had unwittingly followed their recommendation but the results were not promising. Why wasn't the marsh vegetation coming back? Was this a failed experiment?

Sharing his concerns with the others, the local engineer encouraged him to visit another re-flooded marsh called Abu Zirig. Conditions there were much better than in Karmashia, he assured Azzam. So after another uncomfortable night at the Genoob Hotel, they drove north across an empty desert that Azzam remembered from his youth as having been productive rice fields. They arrived at the town of Islah on the north end of Abu Zirig Marsh, and after driving through the bustling market square, suddenly Azzam saw that there was water. They stopped and he rushed out of the car and headed toward the fishing boats crowding the shoreline of a large lake. Thrilled with delight, Azzam insisted on hiring a *balam* to go exploring. They boarded, and it puttered and puffed its way into the cool breeze of the marsh.

The Abu Zirig Marsh begins at the terminus of the Gharraf River (a branch of the Tigris), opening out like a fan toward the Euphrates River. Its destruction had been an easy task; the government simply built an earthen dyke across the end of the Gharraf to block the flow of water. In turn, re-flooding had simply required Ali Shaheen's backhoe to dig an incision into the dyke. The returning water had followed its former courses, lapping up against its ancient shores, seeping into the dry cracked ground, gradually soaking further south until a huge lake was formed. But this lake wasn't barren: reeds had started to sprout along the shoreline, in some areas invading the lake in large stands.

Because fishing nets were strung everywhere, the boatman had to periodically lift the motor out of the water so that it didn't get caught in them. He knew everyone on the lake, and the team stopped and talked with many of the local fishermen, their voices ringing over the bright water. The men were catching a lot of fish here, mostly carp, but very small. The group puttered southward through the water and reeds for about an hour and still didn't reach the end of the lake. Finally, they turned back to Islah and then drove toward Nasriya and the Genoob Hotel.

That night, Azzam slept well for the first time in Iraq, comforted by the knowledge that at least one marsh had begun to regenerate reeds.

Driving back to Baghdad the next day with Janabi's engineer, Azzam began to wonder what was happening on the northern side of the Central Marshes, so he stopped in at the village of Maimuna, nestled among the distributaries branching south from the Tigris. As always when he entered a village, he asked to speak with the tribal elders. They told him of a nearby area that had been re-flooded, called the Auda Marsh, and offered him a local man to guide them, so Azzam headed off to explore. He remembered Maimuna as a prosperous town surrounded with lush rice fields and groves of date palms, but now the wind blew dusty clouds from the barren earth as they passed by sparse encampments of people living in mud hovels amidst the desert. The local man told him that the farmers were not allowed to cultivate anything except wheat, which grew so poorly that it did not even bring enough money to pay for the seeds.

For an hour they passed through nothing but dusty fields lying fallow next to empty water canals. Finally they stopped at a pumping station that had been used for extracting groundwater during the last stages of draining the marshes. The guide told him that after the war, looters had stolen the pumping equipment and the locals had breached the embankments along the drainage ditches, allowing water to flow back into the former marsh. As they drove along the levee, Azzam began to see reeds sprouting in low spots and the brown desert slowly turned to green.

They stopped the car at a crudely constructed reed hut: looking inside, they found a group of ragged boys eating their lunch of grilled fish. With typical marsh hospitality, they were invited to partake of the meager meal. Azzam thanked them and handed around bottles of water instead. The youths clambered out of the hut and followed them as they climbed a small dirt hill. As the men gained that vantage point, they were struck by the sight of a vast landscape of deep green rushes stretching out as far as they could see. Finally there was real wetland vegetation—not the towering reeds of the permanent marshes, just the shorter, slender-stemmed cattails more characteristic of the seasonal marshes—but wetland vegetation nonetheless. Not believing that the plants could have grown so fast, he re-checked with the guide: it was true: six months ago this marsh had been desert.

A dozen *mashuf* were pulled up on the muddy shore beneath them, and more were being poled in and out of the marsh. Azzam went down to where they were offloading their catch, mostly carp ranging in length from one to six inches. His guide happily bought ten pounds (4.5 kg) of fish for about two dollars. Azzam wondered why they caught such small fish, and the men confessed that they were using the electrical shock method for fishing.

"That is *haram* (not moral in Islam)," Azzam said.

"No it is *halal* (moral)," they replied, "Because we have nothing else to feed our children."

There were no women around. These were daily fishermen, coming into the marsh to work early each morning, heading back to their miserable mud huts in the desert at night. They said there was one family of water buffalo herders that had set up camp in the marshes, but the general consensus held that there was not yet enough water to support buffalo. The men asked Azzam if he could lobby the government to allow more water into the marsh.

Azzam persuaded one of the fishermen to paddle him in his *mashuf* into the reeds to test the water quality. For the first time since he returned to Iraq, Azzam experienced the marshes he remembered—the cool wind rustling through freshly grown rushes, the dank smell of organic mud, the lazy buzz of flies and an occasional frog croak. Every now and then a bird trilled. He stood up in the *mashuf* at the risk of capsizing it, the guides gripping the plants to stabilize the small craft, and still could barely see above the rushes: the marsh appeared to roll on forever. He wanted to go find the buffalo herders, but time was pressing and it was too dangerous to be traveling at night back to Baghdad amidst the insurgents, so he reluctantly said goodbye.

CIAO ITALIANO

When the New Eden project was created, Dr. Clini had promised Azzam more than money—he also committed Italian engineers to assist him with planning the restoration of the marshes. So in October 2003, Andrea Cattarossi arrived with the first contingent of Italians. Andrea had developed the hydrologic models for the initial work of the Eden Again project, and when he first heard about the New Eden project, he insisted to continue working on this watery paradise that had already captured his imagination. Azzam was relieved to have experienced partners; together, they spent a hectic week meeting with Iraqi government officials and planning out the project. When the other Italians left, Andrea wanted to visit the marshlands, so Azzam took him to see the Auda and Abu Zirig marshes.

The combination of Azzam and Andrea in the marshlands created a synergy of fast-paced ideas. Observing the flow regime through Abu Zirig marsh, they immediately realized that additional water regulators would be necessary to optimize its restoration. Designing the regulators would require a detailed modeling study, which in turn demanded additional detailed data on topography and the quantity and quality of available water. So they developed a plan to study the present conditions in the marsh and develop the necessary data upon which to base the model. They agreed that the Iraqis would conduct the field work, Andrea would complete the modeling, and then they would work together with the MoWR to design the regulators.

Andrea was appalled by the enormous waste of energy represented by the immense gas flares of the oilfields around the marshlands, and heartbroken by the throngs of children who ran after their car begging for water bottles. Together he and Azzam dreamed of a system where the flared gas, instead of being wasted, would be used to fuel water-treatment plants that would provide safe drinking water for the marshland communities. In those days, anything seemed possible; their imagination knew no bounds.

GROWTH OF AN ORGANIZATION

Unfortunately Azzam's money was more limited than his imagination. By October, he had completely exhausted the small grant from the Wainwrights, and the Italian funding was still winding its way through the international banking system. The Iraq Foundation was undergoing its own funding difficulties, awaiting monies from another large USAID contractor. Meanwhile, Rend Rahim had taken a sabbatical from the Foundation to serve as Iraq's ambassador to the United States. By chance Azzam ran into her at a restaurant in Baghdad and borrowed money from her own purse to pay for his living expenses. In November, the New Eden grant finally arrived in the Iraq Foundation bank account, and Azzam quickly set about hiring staff to complete the ambitious projects he and the Italians had proposed.

He visited the Civil Engineering Department at Mustanseriya University in Baghdad, where he asked the professors for their best students and promptly hired them: Abbas and Saif. A week later, two other young men showed up at the Iraq Foundation office and sheepishly announced that they also wanted to work for Azzam.

"We are from Mustanseriya University, and we heard about your project from our friends that you hired last week. They are the best students in the class and we are … not the best. But we don't mind going to the marshes, we will perform any hard labor you ask, and you have to hire us." So Waleed and Ra'ed[9] joined Azzam, and they proved to be good practical engineers.

Azzam needed someone to supervise the engineers and oversee the scientific work. Rend recommended Dr. Jamal Abayachi, a professor at Baghdad University and a prominent expert on Iraq's water quality. Azzam met him at his university office, where pigeons perched atop his ancient and unusable computer. They agreed on a salary of $1,200 a month—high by Iraqi standards, but Azzam desperately needed help. He had no desire to remain a one-man show; he needed partners to help him build a lasting and sustainable organization.

Three weeks later, a huge car bomb exploded near the Iraq Foundation office, which was located adjacent to the Green Zone. Then a mortar fell, unexploded, onto the lot next door. Sensing the growing danger of living so close to the CPA, the nascent group decided to move to new offices in the Mansour District. Azzam purchased a generator because the central power grid went off every few hours, a satellite Internet connection to communicate with the rest of the world, and computers and desks for the staff. The Italian funding rapidly dwindled.

In addition to the technical staff, a full security detail proved necessary—a total of seven guards, with two men per eight-hour shift and a supervisor. They mostly sat in the kitchen or on the front porch, smoking and drinking small cups of boiled coffee. But these hired guns were an essential expense: assassinations and kidnappings happened every day, and although the American newspapers only reported incidents involving westerners, the vast majority of the victims were Iraqi.

---

[9] Ra'ed was killed in a drive-by shooting in the sectarian violence of 2006. His colleagues still mourn his loss.

CONSERVATION CONSPIRACY

"Dr. Azzam, can you come down to Chubayish?" Jassim Asadi asked him in December 2003. "I really need to talk to you, could you please visit us soon?" Azzam drove down the next week and met him in Ali Shaheen's office, and together they drove east towards the dried Chubayish marsh. Jassim explained that although many other areas had been re-flooded, his own beloved marsh remained dry; no one had taken any action because the marsh dwellers were all long gone, exiled to other parts of Iraq.

"Can you help us?" Jassim asked.

The three men stood on the elevated roadway looking south at the Euphrates River. Rain had fallen abundantly in the Turkish highlands that year, and the water level in the Euphrates was very high. They turned north toward the Chubayish marsh and observed that it was completely dry—no water, no reeds, no fish—just hard, dusty soil. They could also see that the level of the ground in the dry marshes was lower than the water level of the Euphrates. They began to discuss what could be done to return water to this marsh. They decided that there was no need for a big project; if the embankment they stood on was cut, the water would flow directly from the Euphrates into the marsh. Historically, the Central Marshes received most of its water from the north through tributaries of the Tigris River, and then water flowed southward from the Chubayish Marsh into the Euphrates. But now that the Central Marshes were dry, water from the Euphrates would tend to naturally flow northward and re-flood the Chubayish Marsh.

Jassim asked Shaheen if his office, the local Ministry of Water Resources, could do the earthwork, and Shaheen replied that it was difficult. Now that the central government was in control again, he would need to get permission for this action. It could take a long time and possibly not be approved.

Jassim did not like this course of action. He had waited long enough. "If you let us borrow your excavator," he promised, "We will say we don't know who broke this embankment; this will be a secret between us. But we must make this marsh good for the local people." Shaheen agreed to send an excavator, Azzam determined the best locations for the breaks in order to maximize the water flow, and Jassim provided labor from the local tribesmen.

The next day the excavator made incisions at three locations in the dyke and the water came flowing from the high Euphrates, spreading northward over the dry land. A small crowd gathered to witness the event, and they celebrated in the traditional style, young men dancing the war dance, shooting guns in the air, the women ululating with tears in their eyes.

MIXED RESULTS

Azzam went south again in January. The previous October, Karmashia Marsh had appeared as little more than a pool of stagnant water swallowed up by the surrounding desert. This time, Azzam was flabbergasted to find the entire area re-flooded, its green reeds stretching out to the horizon. The marsh dwellers had followed fast behind the restorative water, appearing from out of nowhere, walking along the same embankment Saddam had built for his security forces to evict them. At least 100 families had already built reed huts on the side of the elevated roadway. Most of them had dug out soil from the embankment itself to form a building pad down lower next to the marsh, but some had built directly on top of the roadway. Apparently it worked for them, but the embankment was getting smaller and smaller, making it difficult for vehicles to pass through.

Disembarking from his Land Rover, Azzam talked to the people who gathered around. He learned that most of them had spent their internal exile further upstream on the Euphrates, earning their living as servants to the wealthy landowners there. They returned herding cattle in front of them, but eagerly sought to trade their livestock for water buffalo, which were better suited to living in the marshlands and provided more valuable dairy products.

Fishing was the most important economic activity and, as in Abu Zirig, they were using electric shock methods. The former security roadway served as a transportation corridor to take their fish to market. Every day, trucks drove in from Basra and Nasriya to collect the fish, and the marsh dwellers bartered their catch for drinking water and gasoline for their generators. When asked why they needed generators, the men pointed to the satellite television dishes atop their reed huts. Azzam marveled at their priorities as he watched their children wander about barefoot in the cold mud.

Next, Azzam drove to the Chubayish marsh to see how Jassim's re-flooding project had progressed. Standing on the embankment, he could see a steady flow of mud-brown river water streaming northward through the breach. Looking further out, he could see the water turn an alarming rust-red as it flowed over the parched earth of the dried marshes. He had been accurate in his engineering; a huge amount of water flowed into the dried marshes, and the ghastly red water extended to the horizon. But nothing grew in that water, not even fuzzy algal scum. They had created a toxic wasteland.

Panic struck Azzam's heart. What had he done? Was it possible his actions had made matters worse? He had no answers. Only time would tell if the re-flooding had been heroic or foolish. He returned to Baghdad with a heavy heart.

USAID RETURNS WITH SCIENTISTS

The long-awaited second USAID expedition began in February 2004. Initially planned for a greatly expanded scientific team, there were only two new members. One was Dr. Edward Maltby, a well-respected wetlands scientist who joined the team through funding from the British Department for International Development (DFID). He had acted as the principal investigator for AMAR Appeal's 1994 study and also served as an essential member of the Eden Again scientific panel in 2003. An Australian agricultural soil expert, Dr. Rob Fitzpatrick from Australia's Commonwealth Scientific and Industrial Research Organization (CSIRO), also joined the team.

On the first expedition, Azzam had constantly clamored to visit Chubayish but now he did not want these scientists to see what was happening in the marshlands he and Jassim had re-flooded, afraid that perhaps he had ruined the land forever. *Let nature take her course,* he reassured himself, *conditions will improve,* but he still had a nagging worry that they had made a terrible mistake.

The team spent two days exploring the Hawizeh Marsh. Azzam had not visited this area on his own because of the higher risk of banditry in these sparsely-populated border marshes, so he was glad that the USAID security team offered a secure opportunity to survey them again. Northern Hawizeh, which had never been dried, still looked as robust and vibrant as it had in June 2003. There was plenty of water, plenty of reeds, abundant fish and of course numerous fishermen in their *mashuf*.

The drying of southern Hawizeh had begun in the 1980s to prepare for development of the Majnoon oilfield, and the area had deteriorated further during the Iran-Iraq war as battles raged back and forth across the border. At the time of the first USAID expedition, it had remained dry, its flat land dotted with mounds of earth that formerly housed artillery installations. But now the second expedition found an extensive lake covering the dust that they had seen in June. As had occurred elsewhere in southern Iraq, the local inhabitants had broken the embankments that held back the water in hopes of re-creating their former fishing grounds. But re-flooding this dried marsh had merely created a huge lake where nothing grew except for a few spindly reeds sprouting along the shoreline. The ample amount of water itself may have been to blame: water depth ranged between six to nine feet (1.5-2.5m), which may have been too deep to allow for sunlight to initiate germination of the seeds.

Fish had migrated to the lake with the water from the river, and fishermen eagerly paddled through the waters in their slender *mashuf.* Azzam had witnessed the miracle of re-growth at the Auda and Karmashia marshes, so the lack of immediate re-growth here did not bother him as much as it did the other team members. At least the water was not bright red, and the presence of abundant aquatic life was reassuring. But Dr. Richardson remained extremely pessimistic about the prospects for restoration. He summarily concluded that the re-flooding of southern Hawizeh would simply create an ephemeral salt pond similar to what they had seen at Sanaf, the seasonal marsh north of Hawizeh, in June of 2003.

Azzam was very concerned, however, by the sight of large earth-moving equipment along the international border far in the distance. Borrowing Dr. Maltby's binoculars, he could see that the Iranians were building a huge dyke along their side of the frontier. The embankment could serve only one purpose: the Iranians wanted to stop the flow of water from the Karkheh River into the marshlands on the Iraqi side. The dyke signified trouble for Hawizeh; water from the Karkheh had largely sustained it during the drying of the 1990s and remained vitally necessary for the wetland to thrive and prosper.

Azzam was duly impressed by the expertise of Drs. Richardson's and Maltby, but he also realized the increasing danger posed to western scientists working in Iraq. Although Peter Reiss promised to continue the expeditions on a periodic basis, Azzam correctly predicted that neither Richardson nor Maltby would return to the marshes in the near future. To continue the scientific program and access the scientists' extensive experience in restoration, Azzam proposed that his Iraqi team implement the necessary field work, after which the western experts would help evaluate the data and provide guidance for additional steps. This method of sharing the project, he thought, would benefit the western scientists, the Iraqis, and the marshlands.

So Azzam submitted a proposal to DAI for monthly ecological sampling in three marshes—Karmashia, Hawizeh, and Abu Zirig. DAI reviewed the proposal and greatly reduced both the number of sampling points and the proposed budget; eventually they agreed to pay for only six sampling points in an area covering over 3,000 square miles (7,700 km^2). Azzam argued to maintain the proposed sampling strategy, to no avail. Fortunately, IMELS agreed to fund an expanded sampling program in the Karmashia and Abu Zirig marshes to obtain the necessary data to allow the Italian engineers to design improved water control structures in those locations.

THE REAL FIELD WORK BEGINS

In March 2004, Dr. Corrado Clini arrived in Baghdad amidst daily bombings, mortar attacks, and assassinations to announce an extension of the New Eden project. Then the real work began. Andrea Cattarossi and his American boss, Doug Hamilton, along with Italian engineer Paolo Ruffini, had come to Iraq in January and spent several weeks collecting existing background information and familiarizing themselves with the marshlands. Now the program would become more organized, implementing real work in the field. The marsh dwellers had initiated action by re-flooding their marshes: the scientists and engineers would now do their part to help ensure a successful restoration.

Another contingent of Italians showed up in March to help train staff for the Abu Zirig study. The trainees included the four engineers that Azzam had hired for Nature Iraq, along with staff members from the Ministries of Environment and Water Resources. The cultural differences posed no problem—both Italians and Iraqis tend to be loudly gregarious, and the two groups greatly enjoyed each other's company. But none of the Iraqis spoke Italian and vice versa, so they attempted to communicate with each other in broken English, with Azzam spending much of his time translating between the two groups.

The training began in Baghdad, where the Italians tried to teach the Iraqis to use computer spreadsheets to record and analyze the data they would be collecting in the field. Because computers had been highly regulated under the previous Ba'ath police state, the Iraqis' skills in such basic programs as word-processing and spreadsheets ranged from poor to nonexistent.

The training deteriorated further when they traveled down to Abu Zirig to learn field techniques. Iraqis regard any form of manual labor as lowly and demeaning. Iraqi gentlemen wear freshly-shined leather shoes and western-style business suits at all times and they never get their hands dirty. As highly-regarded members of the upper echelon of society, university professors never went into the field, and therefore their students lacked practical training. For generations, the scientists of Iraq had stayed in their offices and sent uneducated technicians out to collect samples. As a result, no one had any kind of common sense when it came to collecting samples.

The former government had also outlawed the possession of local maps, so the Iraqis had little sense of how to locate themselves on a scientific chart. They became lost in the labyrinth channels of the northern marsh and had to be led out by local fishermen. From then on, local guides were considered essential members of the field team. All the technical apparatus was new to the Iraqis, but eventually the Italians trained them how to use the equipment. The Iraqis then ran the field program for the next year, with monthly sampling at 40 locations in the marsh for water quality, water flow, and ecology. The Italians monitored the marshes via remote sensing analysis and invited some of the Iraqis to Italy for further ecological training using the Po River Delta and the Venetian Lagoon as field locations and examples of successful restoration.

Dr. Jamal Abayachi turned out to be one of those professors who would not get his hands dirty; he flatly refused to even go in the field with the Italians. Instead, he recommended that Azzam hire his friend, Dr. Ali Douabul, to lead the field work while Abayachi managed the office. Douabul had trained in Iraq but had worked outside the country for a number of years. Azzam interviewed him and offered a salary of $1,500 a month. Douabul refused.

"I've been working with Jamal Abayachi for 20 years and I've always done 90% of the work," he said. "You'll see that I work twice as hard as him, so I deserve twice his salary." Azzam acceded, satisfied to add an enthusiastic, practical manager to the team.

A few weeks later, Douabul drove south with the four engineers, as well as three new scientists he had hired to begin the ecological monitoring for IMELS and USAID. Azzam could not accompany them, and it broke his heart. Just as the real science was about to begin, he had been called to New York for a United Nations Sustainable Development conference. Dr. Clini wanted to establish a Sustainable Development Partnership between Italy and Iraq, and it was Azzam's job to ensure that the requisite affiliations were developed so that his fledgling group received the necessary resources to continue its work. Everyone had to play their assigned role in marshland restoration, and the job of politician and spokesperson had apparently fallen to Azzam.

That role kept him very busy in 2004. In January he presented the keynote speech at the annual meeting of the Everglades Coalition in Florida, taking the opportunity to wade appreciatively through their vast wetlands and witness true team-building in action. In February he was called to testify in front of the House Foreign Relations Committee regarding the restoration of the Iraqi marshlands. In March, Yale requested a seminar. April found Azzam first in New York and then China for sustainable development conferences. In May he addressed the Mountain Film Festival in Telluride, Colorado. He presented a technical paper at a scientific symposium at a conference of the International Association for Ecology in Utrecht in July, and then in August he flew to Tokyo to assist with starting up the UNEP marshlands project. October found him addressing a major symposium at Harvard University. It seemed that the entire world wanted to help restore the marshes, or at least wanted a piece of what promised to be a multi-billion-dollar project.

At Harvard, Azzam hired another key member of the Nature Iraq team—Anna Bachman, an American environmental scientist. Anna had first visited Iraq with a peace team in December 2002, and after the war, memories of the people she had left behind tugged at her heart, yet she could find no official capacity in which to help them. In 2003, this fearless young woman quit her job, withdrew her meager life savings and traveled solo to Iraq. With a Master's degree in environmental science, she decided to address environmental health issues in post-war Baghdad. She stayed on in Iraq for six months until her money ran out, but her enthusiasm never flagged. Probably the world's most stubborn woman, she refused to give up on the chaotic country and had come to the Harvard conference to beg Azzam to be part of Nature Iraq, eventually becoming an indispensable senior staff member, ten years later still living in Iraq and serving as Nature Iraq's Director of Conservation.

Since its founding in 2001, the Eden Again and then the New Eden projects had operated under the umbrella of the Iraq Foundation, but by the end of 2004 it was becoming clear that the work had outgrown this arrangement. The Iraq Foundation's main mission focused on human rights, democracy, and humanitarian projects; scientific work was not within their primary purview. Iraq's new constitution allowed for the formation of non-profit organizations, so Azzam went to the newly-formed Ministry of Civil Affairs and registered his group under the name "Nature Iraq." With field operations beginning, the nascent organization needed more space for processing and analyzing environmental samples, so they moved out of the Iraq Foundation offices and rented their own building.

Iraq's first environmental organization was well on its way.

7. NATURE HEALS HERSELF

Enki, the fate-decreeing king ... collected all the waters, established their dwelling-places, let flow at his side the life-giving waters that begat the fecund seed, suspended at his side the Tigris and Euphrates ... The lord Enki organized the marshes, made grow there reeds young and old, brought fish and birds into the marshes, swamps, and lakes ... and charged them with supplying the abundance of the gods.

—The Debate between Bird and Fish (Sumerian, circa 2000 BC)

In June 2003, Hassan Partow joined the flow of Iraqi expatriates returning to help rebuild their homeland. As part of UNEP'S Post-Conflict Unit, he struggled to set up a makeshift office at the Canal Hotel in Baghdad under terrible working conditions. Traffic was a daily nightmare—driving from one side of the city to another could take hours. The electricity went off and on, Internet service flickered intermittently, and air conditioning was nonexistent. Partow wanted to accomplish so many goals, but it was almost impossible to get anything done. He fell into bed exhausted every night but awoke the next morning exhilarated by the opportunity to finally assist his suffering countrymen.

He desperately wanted to visit the marshes and see conditions there for himself, but more pressing issues constantly demanded his attention. Bombing campaigns, along with post-war looting, had seriously compromised the integrity of Iraq's chemical facilities. Avoiding potential releases of hazardous chemicals and radioactive waste into the environment had to be his top priority. Months went by as he worked to protect the people of Baghdad from suffering yet another devastating catastrophe. He kept telling himself *later, next week, next month, I will start work in the marshes.*

On the afternoon of August 19, 2003, Partow left his office to attend a meeting with another UN agency. As he drove across town, a suicide bomber parked a flatbed truck in front of the Canal Hotel and detonated a 500-pound bomb. The blast ripped through the building, killing 22 people and seriously injuring more than 100 of Partow's co-workers and friends. He was evacuated a day later along with most of the UN staff. As of 2012, UNEP has never officially returned to Iraq.

MONITORING THE MARSHLANDS FROM AFAR

The loss of so many of its staff brought UNEP'S Post-Conflict Unit to a standstill, and it took some time for the agency to re-direct its efforts. The team returned to Geneva and attempted to help Iraq's dysfunctional government resolve its most critical environmental emergencies. But the bureaucratic tree of UNEP has many branches, and its International Environmental Technology Center (IETC) in Japan developed a proposal for introducing Environmentally Sound Technologies to the marshlands, and Japan's International Cooperation Agency (JICA) agreed to fund the project. This program dealt mainly with providing safe drinking water and developing pilot projects for the treatment of wastewater in the towns surrounding the former marshlands. A large portion of the funding was expended in conferences and educational tours held outside Iraq. Dr. Chizuru Aoki from IETC was selected as the Project Coordinator, and she hired an Iraqi, Dr. Ali Lami, to serve as the National Coordinator for the project and oversee its work inside Iraq.

Exiled from Iraq, Partow still could not forget the marshes. Eventually he realized that, just as he had documented the destruction of the marshes, he could use remote sensing observations to track their recovery. He developed a program for satellite monitoring of the marshlands and successfully lobbied for funding under the IETC program. If he couldn't get his feet wet on the ground in Iraq, the program he dubbed the Iraqi Marshlands Observation System (IMOS) nevertheless allowed him to track from the sky the rapid changes taking place in the marshlands.

So every week for three years, Partow's technical team received and processed images; every week they observed astounding improvements in the marshes. The re-flooding began in March 2003, as soon as the Ba'ath government fell, and it spread rapidly over the next three years as locals continued to breach the dykes and dams constructed by the former regime. By the time UNEP ended its remote sensing project in

2006, re-flooding had restored 58% of the marshes' 1970s level. The combined area of freshwater lakes and marshes increased from 300 square miles (800 km^2) in the beginning of 2003 to over 2,100 square miles (5,500 km^2) in 2006.

A consistent pattern emerged as each area was re-flooded. At first, the dry land was replaced by an open-water lake. Then wetland vegetation began to grow around its shoreline and on shallow banks within the lake. Eventually, the steady growth of reeds resulted in emergent marsh vegetation supplanting the open-water lake. None of the 1,300 square miles (3,400 km^2) of new marsh vegetation required human intervention, no one planted seedlings or even reseeded at all—an astounding achievement for the world's largest (and most disorganized) wetlands restoration project.

BIODIVERSITY FIELD WORK: ENTER THE CANADIANS

While the IMOS project adequately monitored the progress of re-flooding and re-vegetation of the marshes, it could not fully illuminate the details of the flora and fauna living in the recovering ecosystem. Sidelined by the sectarian violence in Iraq, the western scientists constantly asked questions: What did the marshes really look like on the ground? What types of plants were growing? Had healthy, robust and diverse wetland communities reformed, or was the vegetation merely struggling to survive? Had the fish populations recovered? Were native species returning, or was the population dominated by non-native invasive species? Had the endangered birds survived the drying, were the migratory flocks returning, had nesting colonies been re-established? Had any mammals returned or had the threatened species become extinct?

Having been isolated from the western academic world for 30 years, none of the scientists remaining in Iraq possessed the resources to carry out the necessary studies to answer these questions. Discouraged by the former Iraqi government from studying environmental ecology—especially those ecosystems, like wetlands, that the regime intended to destroy—Iraqi biologists had been forced to limit themselves to taxonomical and laboratory studies, and lacked any competence in ecological field studies. So when the Canadian International Development Agency (CIDA) expressed interest in supporting marsh restoration, Azzam steered them toward ecological work.

The first Canadian involved in the Eden Again project was Clay Rubec, one of the government's senior experts on ecological restoration and international wetlands issues. He first met us in 2002, when Azzam, Michelle, and I presented our preliminary scientific work at a symposium he was chairing at the Global Biodiversity Forum in Valencia, Spain. Rubec proved vitally essential to our success at the meeting, although he had to chuckle at our initial naïveté.

"When I first met them in 2002," Clay remembers, "I thought that the Eden Again group was a bit disorganized, but it was obvious that they sincerely wanted to help the Iraqi marshes. Then in August 2003, I was contacted by Claire Miquet from CIDA. The University of Waterloo had expressed interest in doing environmental work in Iraq, so she organized an interagency meeting and to my surprise, there was Azzam Alwash, making the case for our involvement in restoring the Mesopotamian Marshlands."

Azzam's enthusiasm provided additional momentum for the project, and CIDA recommended further study of how Canada could help restore Iraq's environment. But their government had not yet sent a diplomatic mission to Iraq, and thus still banned its employees from entering the country. For CIDA to undertake a project, the challenge would be how to work in Iraq without actually going there, and how to keep the project more Iraqi than Canadian.

While the University of Waterloo struggled to develop their official proposal for CIDA, Rubec began to conceive his own project ideas. In March 2004, he visited BirdLife International, a nonprofit group that serves as an umbrella to the world's birding organizations (including the Audubon Society), to ask advice on the most effective course of action. He met with two leading experts on Middle East wildlife, Richard Porter and Mike Evans, who strongly recommended that Canada help the Iraqis survey the Important Bird Areas (IBAS) designated by Birdlife in southern Iraq that had not been studied since the 1970s.

Rubec next met with Derek Scott at the nonprofit group Wetlands International. Scott had authored the "Directory of Wetlands of the Middle East," which included detailed descriptions of the important wetlands, and their flora and fauna, in southern Iraq, and he recommended that these sites be included in the initial field work. Rubec combined the listing of IBAS and important wetlands to form the idea of a Key Biodiversity Area (KBA) program in southern Iraq.

CONFERENCE IN AMMAN

CIDA's approach to international development work always involves an initial meeting with the local stakeholders to ascertain what type of assistance the country actually wants from Canada. So in June 2004, CIDA brought together 45 Iraqi naturalists, professors and government officials with a cadre of Canadian and international scientists at a project conference in Jordan. The meeting focused on designing an inter-university research and exchange program between the Universities of Waterloo, Basra, and Baghdad. In addition to the main academic work, Rubec had managed to obtain funding for his KBA survey under the umbrella of Waterloo's program. So while the professors developed scientific research programs, Rubec used the conference to search for potential Iraqi partners to conduct the necessary KBA fieldwork.

For several years, Richard Porter had been corresponding with Mudhafar Salim, a birding enthusiast in Iraq, and Rubec quickly connected with him at the meeting. Mudhafar had organized a loose network of birders under the name "Iraqi Nature Conservation Society" (INCS), but the group had not been formally registered under the Iraqi government and lacked a bank account or any references from other donors. These deficiencies made it difficult for CIDA to contract directly with INCS. Of course the Nature Iraq team was attending the conference, so Rubec persuaded Azzam to accept a grant from CIDA and pass it through to the INCS.

In November 2004, the first group of Iraqi KBA scientists travelled to Jordan to be trained by some of the world's foremost experts on Middle East wildlife. Canada supported the purchase of a broad spectrum of equipment and supplies for the field biologists from INCS. Rubec helped them refine the list of sites to be visited, and sent them back to Iraq with his best wishes for success.

THINGS GO TERRIBLY WRONG

Most of the field sites had not been surveyed since the 1970s, so INCS decided to conduct an initial visit to just seven selected sites in the southern marshlands in mid-February 2005. The team consisted of Mudhafar, two birders-in-training from INCS, Nature Iraq's fish expert Ibrahem Mhade Abd, two professors specializing in plankton and botany from the Universities of Basra and Dhi Qar, and two female biologists from the Ministry of Environment in Baghdad. The team traveled in two rented Land Rovers, picking up four armed local guides from Chubayish before they started their work. The first day they surveyed the restored marshes in Abu Zirig; the work progressed fairly smoothly, and the team spent the night at the Genoob Hotel in Nasriya.

The second day, they visited sites in Hammar Marsh. The survey lasted longer than anticipated, and it was evening by the time they dropped the guards off at their homes in Chubayish and headed back to Nasriya. Passing through an unpopulated area, the trucks came under fire from two vehicles that forced them off the road. Six armed men emerged from the vehicles, fired their automatic weapons into the side of the Land Rover, and ordered its occupants to get out.

With no weapons of their own, the scientists obeyed the command, but Mudhafar whispered to the women to stay in the vehicle. He suspected that this was not a robbery but a kidnapping, and he had only one priority at that moment: the women could not be taken. He told the kidnappers that the men would go calmly with them if the women were allowed to leave.

The gang briefly discussed the issue, then ordered the KBA team into the trucks and told the driver of the Land Rover to continue slowly with the women toward Nasriya. They then turned their trucks south, crossed the Euphrates, and sped eastward along the dirt embankment on its right-bank levee. Thankful that his equipment in the Land Rover was safe along with the women, Mudhafar began to think about his own survival. He discreetly searched his pockets, removed his INCS business cards and carefully disposed of them through the open window.

Quietly, the scientists whispered amongst themselves: "Don't say anything about the Canadian survey, don't mention the INCS or Iraq Foundation or Nature Iraq. We'll say that we are just a group of students out in the field with their professors." They figured that if everyone behaved cooperatively, they would be held for a few days, ransomed by their families, and then released. Most of them had had friends and relatives kidnapped during the last year of internal conflict, and they believed that if everyone obeyed orders and followed the now-commonplace system of ransom negotiation, no one would get hurt. But if the kidnappers realized the scientists were working with a western government, they might possibly sell their captives to a radical group such as al-Qaeda. These political groups weren't just local thugs interested in ransom money; they obtained funding and staffing from external sources, with the goal of forcing international aid organizations out of Iraq by executing their workers.

The trucks stopped at a remote settlement near the Glory Canal. As they entered a house blindfolded, Mudhafar could hear women and children, but soon the building was emptied. For six days, the frightened scientists shared one room, huddling around a gas heater and sleeping on a bare floor under thin blankets. At first their captors claimed to be an Islamic group searching for a Ba'ath party member in order to obtain revenge for his crimes committed under Saddam; finally they admitted to being mercenaries who kidnapped for money because they thought they had no other way to earn a living.

After a week of relative comfort, the scientists were relocated to a still-dry portion of the central Hammar Marsh, where they stayed in a small, unheated tent for four days while their families in Baghdad finalized their ransom negotiations. Bitterly cold winds buffeted the tent, rain leaked underneath the ground cloth, and the guards refused to bring blankets.

Finally the scientists were loaded onto a truck and driven to a location where they found Mudhafar's uncle waiting for them. In parting, one of the kidnappers asked if the scientists intended to continue their work in the marshlands. When Mudhafar replied in the affirmative, the man laughed. "Don't worry," he said. "You have paid your tax with us: we will not bother you again."

THE WORK MUST GO ON

The abduction put a temporary halt to the field work, but the KBA surveys resumed in the summer of 2005 under the auspices of Nature Iraq and have continued twice yearly since then. Although the government officials at CIDA felt truly devastated by the kidnapping of their Iraqi counterparts, the Iraqi scientists insisted that the KBA work move forward. So CIDA continued to support the program, albeit with a more rigorous security protocol. Initially 42 KBA sites were identified, but a risk analysis indicated that about a third of the locations were located either in areas of heavy fighting or in military exclusion zones; Nature Iraq deemed those sites too dangerous to visit. Another third of the sites were located in the Kurdish region of northern Iraq; because CIDA's program was specifically designated for the marshlands of southern Iraq, these northern sites were not surveyed until 2006, when IMELS contributed to an expansion of the

KBA program into northern Iraq. This left 15 sites in the southern marshlands for the 2005 KBA surveys.

Planning the survey proved a logistical nightmare. No real maps of the former marshlands existed, so Rubec initially provided the team with latitudes and longitudes that theoretically represented the center of each site. A single coordinate made sense for small sites but not for the massive wetlands that covered hundreds of square miles. Finding the wetlands on the ground also proved extremely frustrating; signs appear infrequently on the rural roads of Iraq and none of them indicate the direction to a wetland. To make matters even more confusing, the scientists learned that different tribes have different names for local features. Days were wasted inquiring at local tea shops for directions, stopping people on the road for additional guidance, and still ending up hopelessly lost.

The KBA teams typically included scientists from the Ministry of Environment and university students and professors from the Universities of Baghdad, Basra, Babylon, Dhi Qar, and Sulaymania, along with the regular Nature Iraq staff. The broad-based sampling program meant that each team must include specialists in water quality, botany, fish, macro-invertebrates, and birds, along with technicians to collect soil, water, and plankton samples for laboratory analysis (Nature Iraq's plankton specialists, both married women, requested to work primarily in the privacy of their own homes). In all, each survey typically involved a dozen field staff along with drivers, guards, logisticians, and even more scientists back in the laboratory. Nature Iraq's 2008 KBA Summary Report lists almost 50 scientists who took part in at least one of the surveys.

The KBA team has never again been kidnapped, although they take huge risks every time they enter the field; but to them, risks are an inevitable fact of life in post-war Iraq. Young and capable, they feel themselves immortal. They have gone under gunfire several times in both southern and northern Iraq, and even searched for wildlife amidst bombing campaigns by Iran and Turkey along Iraq's northern border. By 2009, the team ventured into the war zone near Fallujah to canvass the final frontiers of biodiversity in western Iraq. We can only hope that they remain invincible.

OVERVIEW OF RESTORATION FROM 2003 TO 2008

Taken together, UNEP's remote sensing program and Nature Iraq's KBA surveys reveal an astounding story of an ecosystem resurrected. In 2002, UNEP announced that they expected the Mesopotamian Marshlands to completely disappear within five years. Yet five years later, more than 60% of the marshes had been restored—not by any international agency, but by the Iraqi people themselves—with the help of a forgiving ecosystem.

The results have been mixed. Vegetation and wildlife abound in northern Hawizeh Marsh, an area that had never fully dried during the 1990s. Abu Zirig Marsh, which receives a consistent supply of high-quality water from the Tigris River, also flourishes. Fair results have been achieved in eastern Hammar Marsh, where the tides force brackish water in and out of the marsh every day, keeping the water refreshed and oxygenated. But western Hammar and the Central Marshes lack a constant influx and outflow of fresh water—known by experts as hydraulic flow-through—and the stagnant water of these marshes has not yet engendered a robust re-establishment of their ecosystems.

RESTORATION IN THE HAWIZEH MARSHES

From a conservation standpoint, the greatest initial concern of the international scientific community was the maintenance of a healthy ecosystem and wildlife populations in the Hawizeh Marsh. Scientists feared that some species, such as Maxwell's Smooth-Coated Otter— found nowhere else but in Iraq's marshlands—had gone extinct. If a few individuals had managed to survive the destruction of these wetlands, Hawizeh would be the place to find and preserve them. Obviously, saving this last remnant of the huge Mesopotamian Marshlands, its final refuge of biodiversity, was imperative.

During the 1970s, the permanent marshes of Hawizeh covered about 1,000 square miles (2,600 km^2) east of the Tigris River, stretching from Amara to Basra. During the 1990s, the Iraqi government reduced the flow from the Tigris distributaries into Hawizeh and constructed drainage canals and dykes that effectively impounded water within northern Hawizeh while its southern half dried into dust. Water flowing into the marsh from its eastern (Iranian) side kept Hawizeh barely alive for the final years of the century, but in 2000 Iran began infilling the reservoir behind its dam on the Karkheh River, and northern Hawizeh began to die a slow death.

The first IMOS image from February 2003 revealed that northern Hawizeh had shrunk to an anemic wetland covering only about 300 square miles (800 km^2). Surprisingly, a seasonal marsh named Sanaf, just north of Hawizeh, was filled with water. The extent and character of Hawizeh changed little throughout the remainder of 2003. Sanaf slowly dried during the summer, leaving behind a light dusting of salt on the sere mud of its lakebed.

But when the spring floods began in 2004, astounding changes rapidly occurred —floodwaters once again swept across the seasonal wetlands north of the permanent marsh, which itself doubled in size. Noticing the abundance of water, the local people began to break down the dykes that impounded the northern marsh, and water poured through those breaches into southern Hawizeh. Throughout the spring, the marsh dwellers continued to break through the network of earthen embankments that divided southern Hawizeh into a checkerboard of fish ponds. Water cascaded through the widening gaps, and a 200-square-mile (520 km^2) lake appeared seemingly overnight in the formerly dry earth of southern Hawizeh.

Northern Hawizeh flourished between 2004 and 2008. Each spring, the annual floods formed seasonal wetlands at its northern end, expanded its permanent marshes and deepened its open-water lakes. Summer's intense radiation literally commanded the lush growth of vegetation. By fall, evaporation had dried the seasonal marshes, withered the fringes of the permanent marshes, and reduced water levels in the lakes. The wetlands lay dormant throughout the winter until renewed flooding in the spring initiated the next annual cycle.

The conditions in southern Hawizeh caused more concern. For a long time, no plants grew in the huge lake created when the local people broke through the dykes and re-flooded the impoundments. The USAID expedition in February 2004 concluded that nothing would ever grow there; Dr. Richardson predicted that the water would evaporate and form a barren salt flat similar to Sanaf. But nature had other ideas. That summer, green shoots of reeds began to sprout from its muddy shoreline and from shallow banks within the lake itself. Ironically, those shallow banks were actually artificial mounds built by Saddam's regime to house heavy artillery installations during the Iran-Iraq War. Slowly, the deadly knolls became loci for the rebirth of the environment. Over the next two years, wetland vegetation gradually crept outwards from the shoreline and the banks into the deeper portions of the lake. Then in the spring of 2006, reeds rapidly multiplied across most of southern Hawizeh, and a verdant marsh was reborn.

The KBA surveys indicate that Hawizeh Marsh still harbors the largest and most diverse wildlife populations of all of Iraq's southern marshes. Its water quality, while far from excellent, remains superior to any other area in southern Iraq. Salinity is low, and open-water lakes contain adequate levels of dissolved oxygen to support a healthy diversity of aquatic life. Along with an abundance of introduced carp, there are also substantial populations of several species of economically-important native fish. The Arabian Hare *(Lepus capensis)*, an IUCN Red-Listed species, lives among its rushes, as does the Common Otter and, it is rumored, Maxwell's Smooth-Coated Otter, the Grey Wolf *(Canis lupus)*, and the Jungle Cat *(Felis chaus)*.

RESTORATION IN THE CENTRAL MARSHES

While Hawizeh maintained the highest ecological values, the Central Marshes harbored the greatest hope for the revival of the marsh dweller culture. These wetlands historically covered about 1,000 to 1,500 square miles (2,600-3,800 km^2) between the Tigris and Euphrates Rivers, and hundreds of water-based villages nestled within its reed forests. Prior to the 1990s, water had poured into the marsh from the north through labyrinth distributary channels that branched off from the Tigris near Amara, and also surged in over the levees of the Euphrates to the south during spring floods. Saddam constructed the Glory Canal to divert water from the Tigris distributaries away from the marshlands and also built up huge levees to restrain the floodwaters of the Euphrates. By the mid-1990s, the Central Marshes had been converted to a desolate wasteland, and its people—deprived of their watery homes—had seemingly vanished.

Desert scrub dominated the ecosystem of the former wetlands for nearly a decade, but the fall of Saddam's government marked a concomitant change in the environment. Beginning in the spring of 2003, re-flooding was undertaken in three separate areas of the Central Marshes. The first was the Abu Zirig marsh, fed by the Gharraf River at the southwest corner of the Central Marshes. The Gharraf branches off from the Tigris around Kut; it supplies water to wheat and barley fields as it flows southward, finally debouching into the Abu Zirig marsh just north of the Euphrates River. During the 1990s, the Iraqi government installed regulators and embankments on the Gharraf to impede its flow into the marsh, and the wetland subsequently dried. In March 2003, Ali Shaheen pried open the rusty regulators and dug through the earthen embankments, allowing water to once again flow over the parched earth of Abu Zirig. By April 2003, the initial pond had enlarged into an extensive fan-shaped lake. Almost immediately, fresh reeds sprouted from their dry roots underground. The vegetation propagated slowly until the spring of 2004 when a sudden burst of growth expanded across the marsh. The reeds and rushes continued to proliferate through 2005 and 2006, eventually generating a robust recovery of this ecosystem.

Abu Zirig represents the healthiest sub-unit of the Central Marshes due to the high quality of the water it receives from the Gharraf River (water in the Tigris, which feeds the Gharraf, is of far superior quality compared to that of the Euphrates). The low salinity and high levels of dissolved oxygen in its waters nourish an abundant fishery. Non-native carp remain the most abundant species, but the marsh also supports healthy populations of some native fish. Fishing is the primary economic activity here; this lucrative employment has lured back so many marsh dwellers that the increased sewage emanating from the surrounding villages has begun to negatively impact the environment. Birds were also drawn back to the marshes, and the avian population recovered quickly; during 2004 alone, the number of species observed at Abu Zirig doubled from 40 to 80, and the marsh is now considered an Important Bird Area in Iraq.

Several small marshes were also re-flooded along the northwestern edge of the Central Marshes in the spring of 2003, creating open-water areas covering about 40 square miles (100 km²). The largest was the Auda Marsh; wetland vegetation sprouted quickly there, and the marsh was fully recovered by the fall of 2004. Auda was re-flooded through a process the Nature Iraq team laughingly calls the "Ali Baba" method of environmental restoration. During the 1990s, the Iraqi government attempted to desiccate this marsh by depriving it of input from the Tigris River; but the marsh was also being fed by water seeping up from underground, so an enormous pumping system had to be installed in order to maintain dry land. During the rampage of looting in the spring of 2003, thieves pillaged the pumping equipment, and groundwater bubbled up to the surface and rapidly returned water to the marsh. Apparently the roots of the rushes had lingered just underground, and they quickly sprouted once they were covered with water.

In the southern portion of the Central Marshes, the Chubayish marsh just north of the Euphrates remained dry until late 2003, when Jassim Asadi, Ali Shaheen, and Azzam conspired to breach the left-bank levees of the Euphrates and return water to the parched earth. By February 2004, an 80-square-mile (200 km^2) lake had formed. But the water from the river turned bright red as it flowed over the burnt soil of the dried marsh, and not a single plant grew in the ruddy pond for six months. Finally in the summer of 2004, the water began to turn grey and then green as algae populations began to re-establish themselves; then reeds began sending up shoots along the shoreline of the lake and gradually expanded into deeper water. By the summer of 2005, a lush permanent marsh covering about 170 square miles (440 km^2) had been restored.

Although abundant vegetation has sprouted in both Auda and Chubayish Marshes, their water quality remains quite poor. The lack of hydraulic flow-through between the northern and southern portions of the Central Marshes poses a significant threat to their future health. At the present time, water flows into these marshes and simply ponds in the low areas while evaporation increases its salinity and respiration decreases its oxygen concentration. To fully restore the ecosystem, a consistent influx of clean, fresh water is necessary. In the long term, a hydraulic connection between the northern portion of the Central Marshes (Auda Marsh) and its southern part (Chubayish Marsh) must be established or they will both continue to suffer. This connection will not only provide for a continual input of fresh water but will also establish an ecological corridor allowing for natural migration of wildlife between the Tigris and Euphrates riparian populations.

Most of the fish in the Auda and Chubayish marshes are non-native carp; none of the native species have re-established their populations to any great extent because of the water's relatively high salinity and temperature and low levels of dissolved oxygen. Native species are generally more sensitive to poor environmental conditions than the robust non-native carp that have been specifically bred to survive in densely populated fish farms. Fish kills occur frequently in these marshes as a result of low oxygen concentrations. However, large and distinctive populations of endangered and globally threatened avian species both over-winter and breed in the Central Marshes, and they are considered to be one of the most important bird areas in Iraq.

Across Iraq and its neighboring countries, the exiled marsh dwellers heard of the re-flooding of the marshes and began to return to their beloved homeland as early as the spring of 2003. Some of the marsh dwellers moved straight into the marshes, finding their former islands of mud and reeds still elevated above the re-flooded land. But many of the returning marsh dwellers preferred not to live in the marshes themselves. Near Chubayish, most of the marsh dwellers settled down on a small strip of dry land between the Euphrates River and the restored marshlands, just off the main road stretching between Nasriya and Qurna. Living between two worlds, they can paddle daily into the marshes to cut reeds to feed their water buffalo and to weave mats for sale. They can fish and hunt in the marshes for their food while still maintaining relatively easy access to schools, clinics, and markets. By 2006, eight villages had been re-established in this area.

Not every village in the dried Central Marshes, however, desires their restoration. After the Glory Canal was constructed in the mid-1990s, some farmers successfully developed irrigated agricultural fields between the canal and the Tigris River. These communities have expressed a desire to maintain their new lifestyle, and the land has remained dry in accordance with their wishes. In the spring of 2004, unusually high river flows washed away a portion of the levee on the west bank of the Glory Canal, flooding a large swath of agricultural land within the dried Central Marshes. The people in the area had settled into villages of mud huts and were left stranded for weeks until the government was able to repair the levee and control the flooding. At their request, this strip of land has been excluded from any future plans for wetland restoration.

RESTORATION OF THE HAMMAR MARSHES

The Hammar Marshes, the southernmost of the three wetland units, also experienced a miraculous transformation after the fall of the former Iraqi regime. Historically they covered about 1,000 to 1,500 square miles (2,600-3,800 km^2) south of the Euphrates River, spanning the area between Nasriya and Basra. The large, shallow and brackish Hammar Lake, covering about 200 square miles (500 km^2), dominated the center of the marsh. Before they were dried, these wetlands received water from a network of distributaries branching eastward from the Euphrates at Nasriya, and also from floodwaters overtopping the right-bank levees of the Euphrates traversing the northern edge of the marsh. During the 1990s, Saddam's government constructed diversion canals and levees on the Euphrates that completely deprived the marsh of water and it dried completely. In the spring of 2003, local tribes re-flooded Hammar Marsh at several different locations—at its eastern end forming the Garmat Ali and Shafi Marshes; at its western end in an area known as Karmashia Marsh; and most recently at its northern edge near the Euphrates.

The transformation began in April 2003, when marsh dwellers around the settlement of Garmat Ali near Basra broke through the dyke that separated the marsh from its former exit channel, the Shatt al-Basra, which had previously connected the waters of the marsh with those of the Gulf. The huge tidal force emanating from the Gulf pushed brackish water from the Shatt al-Basra up into the dried marsh, where the elevation of the land is actually several meters below sea level. Within a few weeks, a large body of water had formed in the depression where once stood the eastern end of Hammar Lake. In the spring of 2004, another local tribe broke through the right-bank levee of the Shatt al-Arab north of Garmat Ali, and the ensuing flood created a second lake, now known as the Shafi Marsh, of similar size. Ominously, the IMOS satellite images indicated no growth of vegetation in these barren bodies of water for a year. Then in a miracle of nature, plants began to sprout along the shores of the lakes, and by the summer of 2005 the marshes were thriving.

Hammar Marsh was also re-flooded from its eastern end in the spring of 2003, when Shaheen opened the regulators on the Euphrates distributaries. Small ponds of water formed at the ends of the channels and rapidly expanded throughout the summer. Six months later, the Karmashia Marsh covered approximately 100 square miles (250 km^2). Flooding in the early spring of 2004 doubled its size. Finally in 2007, the al-Ghreej clan, who live west of Chubayish, breached the levees on the southern bank of the Euphrates to re-flood the northwestern portion of the Hammar Marshes.

The central portion of Hammar Marsh remained dry throughout 2003. During the floods of spring 2004, the waters of the eastern Hammar Marsh (Karmashia) spread westward, while those of western Hammar Marsh (Garmat Ali and Shafi) spread eastward, until the two sides of the wetlands nearly connected. During the heat of the summer, the fringes of both marsh areas dried, contracting their overall size. The seasonal pattern repeated in 2005 and again in 2006, but the two sides of Hammar Marsh never fully connected with each other.

The Karmashia marsh on the western side of Hammar has the poorest water quality of all the permanent wetland areas. Very little water trickles in from the Euphrates, and depths in the marsh seldom exceed a few feet. The color of the stagnant water ranges from an alarming green to a dismal black; its salinity is high and its oxygen is seriously depleted. Large areas completely dry out during the summer, leaving behind withered reeds and cracked mudflats. Fishing is poor. The area contains only one important KBA, a seasonal lake that attracts migratory waterfowl in the winter and then dries to a salt crust in the summer.

The eastern side of the Hammar Marsh has experienced a much better level of restoration and supports large and diverse populations of both fish and fowl. These marshes are connected to the Gulf, and the tidal currents flush out stagnant water, helping to maintain adequate concentrations of dissolved oxygen. Because of its connection with the ocean, this area is an important habitat for rearing juvenile marine fish that use the reed-filled lagoons as their nursery. The waters are intensively fished by the local inhabitants. Three Red-Listed bird species have been noted here—the Greater-spotted Eagle *(Aquila clanga)*, Eastern Imperial Eagle *(Aquila heliaca)*, and Ferruginous Duck *(Aythya nyroca)*.

Before they were dried, the Hammar Marshes comprised a single ecosystem, where water flowed slowly but consistently from northwest to southeast, from the rivers through the marshes and lakes and into the ocean, but uncoordinated re-flooding has rebuilt an incomplete, disconnected series of separate wetlands. One difficulty with creating a fully-integrated ecosystem is the presence of the supergiant oilfields of Rumaila and West Qurna right in the middle of the former Hammar Marsh. These oilfields effectively block the pathway between the marshes of the west and east. Only a narrow strip of undeveloped land lies between the two oilfields: water could be channeled through that passageway, if enough stream flow were available to span the gap. The lack of sufficient water represents a more intractable problem; a much larger volume would need to flow out of the Euphrates distributaries to flood the wetlands and push their waters all the way through to the Shatt al-Basra. An alternative solution would be to construct a channel linking Karmashia and Garmat Ali marshes; this would allow transfer of water between the units without attempting to re-flood all of the area of the former

1. Typical marshland scene.

2. An open-water lake.

3. A makeshift island dwelling.

4. A permanent village in al-Winais.

5. A *mudhif* in the marshes.

6. Inside the *mudhif*.

7. Baking bread in a mud oven.

8. Water buffalo returning home.

9. Marsh dweller cutting
   reeds for fodder.

10. Marsh dweller weaving reed mat.

11. Deep mud cracks in the dried marshes.

12. Azzam and Suzanne Alwash in the dried Hammar lakebed.

13. A river regulator, open to allow water into the marshes.

14. An embankment breached to allow water into the marshes.

15. An area of dried marsh right after re-flooding.

16. Azzam Alwash monitoring water quality from a *mashuf*.

17. Automatic weapons are required field equipment.

18. Towering reeds in restored marsh.

19. Wild Boar (juvenile) in the restored marshes.

20. Asiatic Jackal in the area of the restored marshes

21. A nest of the Basra Reed Warbler.

22. The Pied Kingfisher.

23. A flock of migratory birds.

24. Fishing using electric shock technology.

25. Women and children gathered for water at Abu Subatt.

26. Marsh dwellers bringing back a load of reeds for weaving.

27. Satellite television dish at a reed hut.

28. Jassim Asadi in the dried marshlands in 2009.

29. Emergent and floating vegetation in the marshes.

30. A woman and her daughter bringing home fodder for the buffalo.

31. Iraq Babbler *(Turdoides altirostris)*.

32. Sunset over Karmashia marsh

Hammar Marsh and thus require less quantity.

Now water enters the Karmashia marsh and simply ponds and evaporates, and the wetlands are becoming increasingly saline. Many indigenous people have returned to their native land, and their livestock (and they themselves when they cannot afford to buy bottled water) must drink from the stagnant marsh. If water could flow steadily from Karmashia through to Garmat Ali and out into the Gulf, salinity would decrease to levels more beneficial for the health of the returned marsh dwellers.

Establishing a continuous flow of water across the entire breadth of Hammar Marsh will not only support the vitality of its ecosystem but also that of the Gulf. Eastern Hammar is the only marsh that has a direct aquatic connection with the Gulf, and maintaining ecological corridors between the freshwater and oceanic ecosystems is critically important for the wildlife of both habitats. Historically, fish and shrimp annually migrated between Hammar Lake and the Gulf for spawning; when the marshlands dried in the 1990s this migratory pathway was disrupted. Reopening the traditional passage for aquatic wildlife will once again allow them to complete their natural lifecycles between the marine, brackish, and riparian systems.

RESTORATION OF THE SEASONAL MARSHES

All three of the permanent marsh areas have been restored to some extent, but many of the former fully seasonal wetlands have disappeared altogether. Historically, each of these wetlands covered about 100 to 200 square miles (250 to 500 km^2), totaling perhaps 1,000 square miles (2,600 km^2), although the extent of seasonal inundation varied from year to year. The Sanniya and Rayan marshes, along the distributaries of the Tigris north of the Central Marshes, used to fill with water every spring but they were long ago developed for agriculture. The Saadiya and Uwaina marshes have been inundated a few times since 2003, but even then they covered only a fraction of their former extents. The seasonal marshes north of Hawizeh have fared somewhat better. Periodic floods inundate the larger Sanaf seasonal wetland north of Hawizeh Marsh, and migratory waterfowl abound in these marshes when they are full. These seasonal resting places represent globally-significant habitats, as the wetlands remain one of the few freshwater systems along this reach of the Siberian-Nile flyway.

FUTURE ISSUES FOR RESTORATION

The resurgence of the Mesopotamian Marshlands is a poignant example of the triumph of nature over tyranny. Yet the return of water to that parched earth does not, by itself, constitute restoration of the ecosystem. True restoration will require decades of dedicated work on the part of its local inhabitants and the public institutions of Iraq, its neighboring countries, and the world. The following chapters address some of the most pressing challenges currently facing the marshlands: the recovery of its natural wildlife, the consistent provision of an ample supply of high-quality water, the implementation of enforceable legal protections, and the sustainable inclusion of the traditional marsh dweller lifestyle within the framework of ecological protection.

8. FLIGHTS OF FANCY

Tuesday, April 13, 2004: We've had a lot of rocket and mortar attacks over the last few days. One day we had eight or nine hits within the wire. As a result, we need to go everywhere in body armor and helmet. So Saturday was a day for birding in "full battle rattle," weapon included, of course … I went to the pond by the junkyard, probably two to three acres of open water surrounded by reeds. There was a lot of commotion in the reeds, with 5 or 6 Dead Sea Sparrows darting in and out … While I was watching them, a large brown warbler hopped up on a reed. It was my second lifer of the day, a Great Reed Warbler.

—Jonathan Trouern-Trend,
Birding Babylon: A Soldier's Journal from Iraq (2006)

On Jon Stewart's Daily Show, comedian Lewis Black was regaling the studio audience with what he termed the Iraq Good News Explosion. "There's good news for Iraqi nature lovers: a newly-formed conservation group called Nature Iraq has published the country's first-ever bird guide," Black boomed in his hearty baritone: "Yes, what a great place to go birding! Hey Maliki, what's say we throw on some camouflage, grab some high-powered binoculars and go lurk? What could go wrong?" he paused while the audience roared with laughter. "Still, you have to admire the optimism of people who can imagine a day when Iraqis will want to see something flying towards them through the air." More laughter followed, the loudest coming from the Nature Iraq staff watching via internet in Iraq, delighted to have their work discovered—and lampooned—on American television.

This field guide, the brain child of BirdLife's Richard Porter and Environment Canada's Clay Rubec, was intended to support and encourage the small yet passionate group of Iraqis who still regularly engage in the hobby of bird watching despite the chaos of continual conflict. The text is written in Arabic with common names in English and species names in Latin. Covering all of the 387 species that have been recorded in Iraq, the volume (published in 2005) represents the first comprehensive field guide to birds for a single Arabic-speaking country.

A year later, Nature Iraq's Anna Bachman discovered a charming book entitled *A Children's Guide to the Birds of Jordan*, published by Jordan's Royal Society for the Conservation of Nature. With their help, *A Children's Guide to the Birds of Iraq*, written in Arabic and Kurdish, was published by Nature Iraq in 2007. A spiral-bound book printed on sturdy cardboard, it is aimed at encouraging young people to appreciate birds and their natural habitats, and has been widely distributed in schools throughout Iraq.

Nature Iraq produced these books to foster the love of birds and bird watching in Iraq and this dream is not as far-fetched as Lewis Black might have imagined. Iraqis prefer to keep birds as pets: many Muslims consider cats and dogs too dirty to allow in the house but avians in cages seem more acceptable. The large pet bird markets in Baghdad continue to draw thousands of bird lovers every weekend, even though they have been the scene of mass murders by suicide bombers during the violence of post-war Iraq.

THE BIRDERS

Conserving Iraq's marshes will require long-term dedicated effort, and developing a national drive toward conservation will take decades of persistent environmental education. Building on the intrinsic attraction of birds is one of the most natural routes to developing a national ethos for ecosystem conservation. When people feel connected to wildlife, they become more concerned for its welfare and the preservation of its natural habitat. Birding clubs naturally drift toward conservation.

One of Nature Iraq's experts on the birds of the marshes is Omar Fadil, born into a family of bird lovers under the repressive regime of Saddam Hussein. His childhood home was a sanctuary of wildlife, filled with all kinds of birds—finches, love birds, parrots, singing canaries, bulbuls and babblers. In addition to dozens of individual cages, his family kept an aviary in the garden to house their racing pigeons and a special falconry for their birds of prey. Somehow they managed to provide for all of their beloved pets throughout the lean years of sanctions and the subsequent turbulence of war and conflict. At one point in 2004, the American military entered Omar's family home during a routine door-to-door search for weapons. After ensuring that the household was safe, one astounded American soldier could not help but exclaim, "Is this a home or a zoo?"

As a small boy Omar's father gave him an encyclopedia of Arabian birds, which he slept with every night, carefully memorizing the distinctive plumage and characteristics of each species. He was a good student and his secondary exams qualified him to attend dental school, but he chose to pursue a degree in biology so that he could expand his ornithological skills. After graduation he undertook his compulsory military service, managing to transform troop patrols into bird-watching tours.

"I saw many birds when we were out on military exercises, but I did not have any books with me to identify them," Omar remembers, "so I would just observe the birds and draw them. I even created my own names for them." At the conclusion of his military service, Omar returned as an instructor at the University of Baghdad. In 2004, he heard about Nature Iraq's KBA surveys and begged to join the team as a bird specialist.

CHASING THE WINTER MIGRANTS

Water birds such as ducks, geese, grebes, cormorants, herons and pelicans depend on aquatic habitats for their life cycles. But lakes and ponds are rare in the arid desert and steppe of central and western Asia. Therefore the Mesopotamian Marshlands, the largest wetlands in the Middle East, constitute a key rest stop along the West Siberian-Caspian-Nile Flyway. When the weather grows too cold up north, huge flocks of grey geese, shelducks, gadwall, wigeon, mallard, shoveller, pintail, garganey, teal, pochard, grebe, and coots converge on the marshlands, eager to feast on the bounty of the wetlands as the winter rains and spring snowmelts begin to swell their shores. Experts have estimated that two-thirds of West Asia's wildfowl spent their winters in the Iraqi marshes before they were desiccated.

Prior to the KBA work, the most recent bird survey in the marshlands was undertaken in 1979 by Derek Scott and Erik Carp. That expedition discovered a stunning profusion of birds, recording over 324,000 individual waterfowl of 79 species, including 3,300 pelicans, 1,850 flamingoes, 2,340 geese, 155,000 ducks, 128,000 coots, 16,600 shorebirds and 13,400 gulls and terns. As the team visited only about 10% of the total marsh area, they concluded that the actual number of waterfowl in the Mesopotamian marshes at that time probably amounted to several million.

With the return of the marshes since 2003, these birds have come back in ever-increasing numbers. The KBA surveys continue to document their recovery, assisted by BirdLife International's Richard Porter, who verifies their identifications and counts through photographic evidence. During the winter of 2008, Nature Iraq counted 20,000 water-dependent birds at 25 observation points in the marshlands. During the 2010 survey, the team enumerated 7,000 Greater Flamingos, 30,000 Northern Shovelers *(Anas clypeata)*, 23,000 Marbled Ducks *(Marmaronetta angustirostris)*, 19,000 Greylag Geese *(Anser anser)*, 9,000 Red-crested Pochards *(Netta rufina)*, 2,500 Ferruginous Ducks *(Aythya nyroca)*, 6,000 Black-tailed Godwits *(Limosa limosa)*, and 6,000 Pygmy Cormorants *(Phalacrocorax pygmeus)*.

One of the most charismatic water birds overwintering in Iraq is the Great White Pelican *(Pelecanus onocrotalus)*. With a wingspan of more than eight feet (3 m), it is one of the largest flying birds in the world, walking clumsily on land but gliding elegantly through the air. The pelican migrates into Iraq each winter to escape cold weather back north, travelling in large flocks containing hundreds of birds. During the 1940s, Thesiger observed enormous waves of soaring pelicans so dense that they blackened the sky. After restoration of the marshes, these insouciant fishers have returned but still not in the numbers that Thesiger probably witnessed; about 2,000 were counted during the KBA survey of winter 2008, roughly comparable to the 3,300 found in 1979.

Pelicans eat only fish; adults of the species require several pounds (1 kg) of it per day. In Iraq, suitable concentrations of fish are found only in the larger lakes of Hawizeh and eastern Hammar marshes. In those locations, pelicans have often been observed hunting in groups, a rare behavior amongst birds. In cooperative feeding, a dozen pelicans arrange themselves in a horseshoe formation on the water; they surround the fish and drive them toward the shallower water, flapping their wings to stir up the mud and then thrusting their bills into the water to catch the fish as they rise gasping for air. Long ago, marsh dwellers observed this method of fishing and developed a similar method using underwater corrals constructed of finely-woven nets instead of pouches to capture their prey.

A surprisingly common visitor to the marshlands is the pinkplumaged Greater Flamingo *(Phoenicopterus roseus)*, the iconic avian of more tropical realms. Large flocks of these gaudy birds overwinter in the marshlands of Iraq, pushed there by extremes of cold weather, flooding, or drought in their breeding habitats of central Asia and southern Europe. They live in saline wetlands, feasting on the brine shrimp that imparts their distinctive pink coloration.

Flamingoes only migrate under cover of darkness, sometimes covering up to 300 miles (500 km) in one night. Failing to find them during the initial KBA surveys, Omar decided that a nocturnal vigil would be required to determine if they had returned to Iraq. "One time the Nature Iraq team went out into the marshes to measure water quality over a 24-hour period, to see the changes through the day and the night," Omar recalls. "I asked to come along, so we camped out overnight with one of the leaders of the local area and two of his men as guards. The night-time marsh was beautiful; we sat in the calmness and watched the wind playing with the reed beds and the fires from the far-off villages. I listened for hours to the call of the Night Heron *(Nycticorax nycticorax)* and the Moorhen *(Gallinula chloropus)*. Then around midnight, I could hear it—the sound of the Greater Flamingo as it migrated overhead, a strange eerie honking, very distinctive to me. The local guy, the leader, I thought he was sleeping but suddenly he jumped up and called his men to attention. While I was listening for the birds, he had noticed the motor of a distant boat. His ears had filtered out all of the natural sounds of the marsh, only listening for human movement. But nothing happened. By the morning, a huge wind we call the *Sharji* began to blow, it ripped up the equipment of the water quality team and we all left. I still have not seen the flamingo in Iraq."

FULL-TIME RESIDENTS OF THE MARSHES

The enormous flocks of migratory birds inspire awe in all who witness them, yet the marshlands also harbor many birds that breed or reside permanently within its sheltering reeds. The Iraqi marshlands represent one of the few locations that Birdlife International has designated as an Endemic Bird Area (EBA). Endemic birds are those that live and/or breed only within a restricted area and are not found in significant numbers anywhere else in the world. Worldwide, only 128 sites have been designated EBAs, with just four located in the Middle

East. The two endemic species in the Mesopotamian marshlands are the Iraq Babbler *(Turdoides altirostris)* and the Basra Reed Warbler *(Acrocephalus griseldis).*

The Basra Reed Warbler spends its winters in sub-Saharan Africa, migrating as far as South Africa, but every summer it returns to the marshes of Iraq to weave its tiny pouch-like nest in the reeds. This is the only place in the world where it is known to breed. When large areas of its wetland habitat disappeared during the 1990s, the IUCN designated the species as Globally Endangered, fearing it might be on the road to extinction. By 2001, it was thought that there were less than 10,000 of the little singers left in the world.

One of the most important locations for monitoring the populations of this species is the Ngulia ringing station in Kenya. During the 1980s and 1990s, their counts for the Basra Reed Warbler declined steadily and significantly, leading them to surmise that its population may have fallen by up to 80% during this time. But because the former Iraqi regime had declared the marshlands a military restricted area, no field work could be undertaken so that the breeding population at its lowest ebb would always remain a mystery.

During the first Birdlife-Nature Iraq training session in 2005, Omar listened carefully to Richard Porter's description of the charming little brown and buff bird. During the KBA surveys, the ornithologists documented many species of birds in the marshes but never obtained a high-quality picture of the warbler as it flitted through the reeds, frightened away by the noise of the KBA team. Gradually an ambition formed in Omar's head: he would be the first person to photograph the elusive Basra Reed Warbler breeding in Iraq.

Omar returned to the marshes alone with a single local boatman. They paddled quietly into the marshes in a small *mashuf* down a narrow channel lined with reeds, silently sliding into the warbler's natural habitat. By now Omar realized that the bird would be nearly impossible to locate by sight, because its earth-toned plumage blends into the surrounding reeds. Instead, he carefully listened for its call as the guide quietly poled the canoe through the reeds. After an hour, he heard a male trilling: *"kaka-kee, kaka-kee, kaka-kee."* It took another half hour to visually locate the tiny bird and follow his darting flight to his nest. Then Omar carefully slid off the *mashuf* onto the damp ground and crept slowly to his goal, a tiny cone-shaped basket strung between a triad of reeds. He settled down to wait for the mating pair and then silently pressed the camera shutter, again and again. He had captured his coveted prey.

Afterward, the Nature Iraq ornithologists continued their surveys in the marshes and found increasingly larger numbers of Basra Reed Warblers. In 2005, the Ngulia ringing station also noted an increase in the number of Basra Reed Warblers captured there, and during the KBA summer surveys of 2008-2010, extrapolations of transect counts estimated the populations in the Central Marshes and Dalmaj Lake alone to be nearly 4,000 pairs. The population apparently rebounded as quickly as its habitat was re-established. "In fact," Birdlife's Richard Porter recently concluded, "the Basra Reed Warbler, currently Globally Endangered, could be given a less-threatened conservation status, if we were not so worried by the dams being built in Turkey on the headwaters of the Tigris and Euphrates. These present the most worrying threat for the future of the special birds of the marshlands."

RARE AND THREATENED

Other significant species of breeding water birds also inhabit the marshlands, including the entire world population of the Middle Eastern subspecies of the African Darter *(Anhinga rufa chantrei).* The marshes have also historically supported isolated populations of two other species that otherwise only occur in tropical Africa—the Goliath Heron *(Ardea goliath)* and Sacred Ibis *(Threskiornis aethiopicus).* These two species breed only in Hawizeh Marsh. When the marshes dried, prominent wildlife experts Derek Scott and Mike Evans concluded that the destruction of their habitat would almost certainly result in the global extinction in the Middle East of the African Darter and Sacred Ibis, and the extinction in Iraq of the Goliath Heron.

African Darters are heron-like birds, up to three feet (1 m) tall, with a very long neck and glossy black plumage streaked with white. They are commonly called "snakebirds" because of their thin necks and the fact that they often swim with only their heads and necks slithering along the surface of the water. They spear their prey while swimming underwater, then flip the fish up in the air and gulp it head first on the way down. The African Darter is a monogamous yet gregarious bird, usually building its nest in large mixed breeding colonies deep in the marshlands.

The Goliath Heron is a magnificent creature. True to its name, its standing height averages around five feet (1.5 m), most of it legs, and it boasts a wingspan exceeding seven feet (2 m), yet it weighs only nine pounds (4 kg). In flight it has a slow and rather ponderous look and, unlike most herons, its legs drag at an angle beneath their bodies, making them easily recognizable in flight. These solitary hunters perch motionless in the reeds of the wetlands, patiently watching for fish or frog; sometimes they also step slowly forward through the mud, with their head held horizontally and neck characteristically crooked, ready for a lightning thrust at some unlucky prey.

The Goliath Heron was a common resident in the Mesopotamian marshes in the early part of the century; Thesiger regularly observed it in the Central Marshes, and Maxwell spied it in the Hawizeh marshes. Sightings of the bird became rarer and rarer, however; only a single one was recorded in six surveys undertaken between 1958 and 1980. Nowadays it is occasionally reported by hunters: it is clearly a very rare bird.

The Sacred Ibis is a species of wading bird that breeds in the marshes and wetlands of Iraq, sub-Saharan Africa, and formerly in Egypt, where it was venerated and often mummified as a symbol of the god Thoth. Adults of the species stand about three feet (1 m) tall, with all-white body plumage accented by dark plumes that hang over their tails, while their heads, necks, and thick curved bills are black. Around 1920, ornithologists observed large numbers of Sacred Ibis in southern Iraq, and Gavin Maxwell reported sighting the distinctive bird on many occasions. But waterbird surveys during the 1970s noted only a few flocks.

During the early KBA training sessions, BirdLife ornithologists emphasized the characteristics and habitats of these birds, along with the significance of finding them in the marshlands. The experienced men knew that finding these species alive in Iraq would create a newsworthy stir. Omar Fadil yearned to be the first to photograph any of these famously rare birds, and he grabbed every opportunity to chase down reports of sightings.

"On one of our trips through Amara," Omar recounted, "our driver met some friends along the way, and we asked them about the local birds. That day, we were looking for the African Darter, they call it *werda* in the marshlands. All of his friends told us, if you want the *werda*, go to the market here, there's a woman selling fish, ask this woman about your birds. So we went to the market and asked the woman if she had a *werda*. She told us no, she didn't, but she had something better to show us at her house. So we went there and under the palm trees by her small reed hut we found three Sacred Ibis. She told us that her husband goes fishing in the marshlands, and

GLOBALLY-THREATENED BIRDS OF THE IRAQ MARSHES
Compiled by Mudhafar Salim and Richard Porter

CRITICALLY ENDANGERED

Sociable Lapwing	Vanellus gregarius	Historically a regular winter visitor, no recent records
Slender-billed Curlew	Numenius tenuirostris	Now probably globally extinct; historically has occurred on migration

ENDANGERED

Red-breasted Goose	Branta ruficollis	Occasional in winter
White-headed Duck	Oxyura leucocephala	Probably a regular winter visitor
Egyptian Vulture	Neophron percnopterus	Occasional passage migrant
Basra Reed Warbler	Acrocephalus griseldis	Endemic breeding summer visitor where recent surveys have shown the population is many thousands

VULNERABLE

Lesser White-fronted Goose	Anser erythropus	Uncommon but regular winter visitor
Marbled Duck	Marmaronetta angustirostris	Widespread breeding resident and winter visitor. Winter counts have exceeded 23,000– the highest concentration in the world
Dalmatian Pelican	Pelecanus crispus	Uncommon but regular winter visitor
Pallas's Fish-eagle	Haliaeetus leucoryphus	Occurred historically in winter but not seen recently
Greater Spotted Eagle	Aquila clanga	Passage migrant and winter visitor
Eastern Imperial Eagle	Aquila heliaca	Passage migrant and winter visitor

NEAR-THREATENED

Falcated Duck	Anas falcata	Recorded once, historically
Ferruginous Duck	Aythya nyroca	Breeding resident, passage migrant and winter visitor
Pallid Harrier	Circus macrourus	Passage migrant
Great Snipe	Gallinago media	Passage migrant but no recent records
Black-tailed Godwit	Limosa limosa	Passage migrant and winter visitor
Eurasian Curlew	Numenius arquata	Passage migrant and winter visitor
Black-winged Pratincole	Glareola nordmanni	Occurred historically, no recent records
European Roller	Coracias garrulus	Passage migrant
Semi-collared Flycatcher	Ficedula semitorquata	Passage migrant

he caught them there, and they are feeding them with the chickens. They keep the Sacred Ibis just to look at, they feel comfortable when they see the wild birds from near the marshes, the same reason I have birds in my home."

Undeterred, Omar persisted in his hunt. "One day in the winter bird survey, I just decided to find a Goliath Heron, one way or another," he recalled. "We had spent three years surveying in the marshes, and the Goliath Heron was one of the most common birds that anybody could observe in the past, before the marshland dried, but still we had not observed it in our surveys. So I went to the police station near the Iranian border, and I was sitting with the officers to say hello and let them know what I was doing there and have a cup of tea with them. If you want to go to the marshes, you must first contact the local police, and then you must find the oldest man around and ask him about the marshes. So I asked an old, grey-haired man about the Goliath Heron. He told me an ancient story about this bird, how one time a Goliath Heron thought the hunter was competing with him, and he killed the fisherman and took his fish from him."

Omar laughed remembering the old man trying to scare him. "So it was like an adventure story. He told me if you are brave enough, you just take the boat from that corner of the reed beds, go left and reach that area which is a big lake, and you can see the Goliath Heron alive in the marshes. He gave us some guides and boats to take us. So I and my colleagues got our equipment and took a journey of two hours boating to get to the area near the Iran-Iraq border, looking for the Goliath Heron. He needs this area, because it has very high reeds where this tall bird can hide. We went for two hours and then found that we cannot get in that area because the reeds are too thick. Then my boat driver, he told me come with me, I know another way, and we circled from the Iranian border, and entered Iran, that means we are sharing the same birds between Iraq and Iran."

"Suddenly, I hear thousands of birds; I can even smell their feces, there is such a huge number. We had found a major nesting colony. The group contained many different species of birds: Little Egret (*Egretta garzetta*), Night Heron (*Nycticorax nycticorax*), African Darter, Pygmy Cormorant, Sacred Ibis, and Eurasian Spoonbill (*Platalea leucorodia*), all nesting there together like a family."

Although most birds nest in pairs, scientists believe that the practice of nesting in multi-species groups such as this may provide better survival against predators due to the larger number of individuals available for defense, as well as the ability to satiate predators. Nesting colonies such as this were commonplace in the marshlands during the middle of last century but had not been observed for decades. Their reappearance suggests that the number of birds returning to the restored marshes had finally reached a critical mass where these nesting colonies could form. The find could also indicate the presence of a healthy population of native mammalian predators such as the Smooth-Coated Otter, Grey Wolf, or the Jungle Cat.

Although Omar exulted in this spectacular find, he remained frustrated in his search. "We have still not found the Goliath Heron. I am thinking that because the tall reed beds are slow to grow, maybe it had to find another territory to nest in, maybe it moved somewhere else. Maybe Hawizeh was its territory before the marshes were drained, and maybe he's looking for better sites of nesting in another place that we don't know. And also I remember this bird nesting alone, they don't nest with other birds, because it needs a large amount of fish, and they don't like competition with other birds. That's my thinking about it: we just have to keep looking."

BIRDS OF PREY

As Omar reminisces about his field adventures, outside on the terrace a hooded falcon cocks its head toward the window; he hears his master's voice. Omar captured the young bird in northern Iraq and has taught it to obey him and hunt on command. He could sell this magnificent raptor for thousands of dollars, a huge sum of money for a young Iraqi. But Omar will never sell this bird. They have a deep personal relationship founded in an ancient cultural history.

Arabs glorify both their horses and their birds of prey. The art of falconry originated in the Middle East thousands of years ago (the practice was brought to Europe in the Middle Ages by returning Crusaders) and has thrived there ever since. Although some people may find the thought of encouraging one animal to kill another distasteful, there are others for whom hunting provides a visceral satisfaction that cannot be supplanted by watching professional sporting events. All of Omar's older male relatives keep falcons and they never miss an opportunity to take them out to practice hunting, even in the midst of the recent civil unrest.

Omar obviously savors the lethality of these finely-tuned hunting birds. "My favorite birds are the falcons. They are very rare in the marshes, because they need the mountains and valleys. They usually perch up high on some kind of tower or rock, so they scan the area looking for their prey. But in the marshes we have found two very rare species. One day we were boating in the eastern Hammar Marshes, and I saw a Grey Heron *(Ardea cinerea)* dive for a fish, and then I saw that the heron was being hunted by a Greater Spotted Eagle *(Aquila clanga)*. Then from out of nowhere there came an Eastern Imperial Eagle *(Aquila heliaca)*, which is even bigger and rarer than the Greater Spotted Eagle. And they started to fight between them for the prey. The winner was the Imperial Eagle. He captured the prey of the Greater Spotted Eagle, who looked sadly behind him as he flew away."

Birds of prey also use the Iraqi wetlands as a wintering area, migrating long distances from Europe and Asia along with the ducks and other waterbirds to reach its fertile waters. The 1979 survey observed over a thousand raptors of 15 species. During the KBA winter surveys at least 14 species of raptor were observed in the marshes. Two of those most regularly recorded are Globally Threatened—the Greater Spotted Eagle and Eastern Imperial Eagle, and the marshes provide an important wintering area for them. Most of these birds ply the wide-open waters of the eastern Hammar Marsh, where the lakes teem with birds and fish and there are few permanent human settlements to disturb them in their relentless hunting.

THE COUNT SO FAR

Nature Iraq's KBA surveys from 2005 to 2011 have greatly increased the scientific world's knowledge of the avian biodiversity of the southern marshlands and have shown that, despite the drainage under the previous regime, no species has become extinct as a breeding bird. Over 285 species have now been recorded in these marshes and their environs of which about 85 breed or are thought to breed. Of the remaining 200 species, 35 are rare visitors or vagrants, and some 165 are regular winter visitors or passage migrants from their Eurasian breeding grounds, relying upon these vast wetlands for resting and refueling on their long migrations. Six species that occur regularly are Globally Threatened and an additional six are Near-Threatened.

HUMAN IMPACT ON BIRDS

The people of the marshlands are both the bird's best friends and their worst enemies. In this area of extreme poverty and widespread hunger, bird hunting remains an economic necessity. But beyond the need to feed their children, the marsh dwellers, like Omar, feel that hunting is a tangible symbol of their cultural heritage worthy of preservation. This connection to their past enriches their present lives. The men of the marsh take great pride in their prowess with guns and they need practice to keep their skills sharp. The local people also prefer the savory taste of wild birds over bland domesticated poultry. Sometimes they even steal eggs from the nests of the wild birds, not to eat directly, but to bring them home to hatch and be raised by their chickens for later consumption.

The KBA team often utilizes the work of the hunter to assist in their species counts. Where the ecosystem has a high biodiversity, local food markets can be found selling 10 to 20 varieties of wild bird—sometimes more than the professional ornithologists could locate in the field. Occasionally they find carcasses of bird species at the market that the team seldom observes in the wild. These are the species that are so shy of humans that the KBA team can easily scare them away. But the patient hunter, eager to feed his family, lies in solitary wait through the long days and nights to secure his catch of the elusive prey.

"The only protectors for these birds are the local people themselves," Omar continues. "If you want to do anything in the marshes you must talk to the locals. Because the people of the marshes give you the security, you can trust them to take you to where the birds are, and where we can find suitable places for observation. The people of the marshes know exactly when the birds come and where to find them and every detail about their life."

On every trip to the marshlands, the team tries to educate the people of the marshes. They cannot tell the people not to hunt and feed their children, but they do teach the people that they should not kill the species that are endangered. They encourage the hunters to let them live and breed because in the future, bird watchers from around the world may come, and their tourist dollars will bring more value than hunting.

"The main thing we do when we meet the local people is to tell them how the birds need their space, how they need their food, we just try to spread our scientific knowledge to the people. Because the locals see the foreign people starting to come from outside the marshes, from Europe and United States and Canada, focusing on their birds, then the idea comes to their mind that these birds are precious. In this way the locals can be the main force behind conserving the birds."

9. FISH FOR THE FUTURE

"My fish, I have built you a home, I have built you a store! ... There is food, food of the best quality ... extending as far as the reed fence. Let your acquaintances come! Let your dear ones come! ... Don't leave your neighbors outside, whoever they may be! ... Enter my fine son .... As if you were in silt settled on the river bed, may you not be able to get up ... and may you not succeed in getting away ... May all kinds of fishes enter with you, my fish ... Nanse, the queen of the fishermen, will be delighted with you."

—"The Home of the Fish," Anonymous Sumerian text (ca. 1000 BC)

Fish are the most important fauna of the marsh ecosystem from a socioeconomic perspective, providing the marsh dwellers with both a readily available supply of protein and a valuable source of outside income. Before the marshes were dried, the UN's Food and Agriculture Organization (FAO) estimated that the total inland catch of fish in Iraq was 21,000 tons (23,600 metric tons), with over 60% of that coming from the Mesopotamian Marshes. These figures do not include fish that were eaten domestically by the marsh dwellers—probably at least double the amount that went to market. Thus the wetland fishing industry represented a vital component of the region's fragile food supply.

During the 1990s, Saddam's early attempts to dry the marshes briefly improved fishing, since the lakes shrank and concentrated their aquatic population, making the fish easier to catch. As the drying progressed, however, the fish inevitably disappeared along with their habitat. In 2003, when the locals re-flooded the marshes, the fish wriggled back in with the surging flood-waters. Olive-green in the river, within a few days their color muted to a soft brown as they readjusted to their ancient home. Fishermen appeared as quickly as the fish arrived, eager to once again be able to provide food for their families.

Superficially, all seemed well with the marshland fishing industry, but in order to ensure that the restoration would have long-term sustainability, Nature Iraq needed to know more than the simple fact that "fish returned." They wanted to determine whether the fish population was sufficiently robust to preserve the natural biodiversity while at the same time allowing for traditional harvesting by the marsh dwellers. Questions abounded. Were the returned species native to the marshlands, or were they invasive foreign varieties that could potentially disrupt the delicate natural food web of the ecosystem? Was the water of adequate quality—temperature, clarity, and salinity—to encourage growth of native species? If not, how could these problems be fixed? Which were the most desirable species from an economic standpoint? Did those desirable fish have a sufficient food supply and appropriate habitat for spawning? Were the fish free to migrate as necessary to fulfill their various life stages, or did their natural pathways remain blocked?

THE FISHERMAN

To answer these questions, Nature Iraq needed an ichthyologist, and Ibrahem Mhade Abd has filled that role ever since the first ill-fated KBA survey. As with most Iraqis, he had suffered deprivation and the constant threat of violence for his whole life: the kidnapping would not deter him from his work. His father grew up in a village in Hawizeh Marsh, and he often entertained Ibrahem with stories of the marshlands. But he also openly opposed the Ba'ath government, and while Ibrahem was still a small boy, the regime executed him and Ibrahem's uncles for their political activities. Left without protection, his mother fled with her six young children to Basra, where young Ibrahem took to fishing to help provide food for his family.

"I soon decided that fish would be the story of my life," Ibrahem remembers. "As a young boy I would go fishing with the other men in the marsh. I loved being with them in the peace and cleanliness of the green reeds, and I was proud to be able to provide food for my family. When I entered college, I chose to study marine biology so I could learn more about aquatic life."

When he began working towards his master's degree at the University of Basra, he wanted to study the fish of the marshes but found that the government did not allow field work there. One day, while out fishing for his dinner on the Shatt al-Arab, he noticed another fisherman using poison to gather his catch.

"He was using an insecticide that is intended for putting on crops, but he knows nothing about this chemical," Ibrahem explained. "I was very disturbed by this situation and wanted to do something that would help convince these fishermen to stop using poison. So I told my advisor that I wanted to make a study on the concentration of poison in the fish and in the blood of the fishermen who are eating their catch. I was thinking that then I could show the fishermen how much poison they are taking into their bodies and tell them: 'If you keep fishing this way, cancer will be the friend of you!'"

In spite of this ardent explanation, his advisor absolutely refused permission for this research, stating that Ibrahem would likely be arrested and imprisoned if he engaged in any study suggesting that problems existed inside Iraq.

"He advised me to stick to a laboratory investigation," Ibrahem complained, "and everyone would be safe. He was a member of the Ba'ath party, so I had to listen to him."

After he finished his Master of Science degree, he found himself dogged by his father's past. Even though Ibrahem was not politically active, Saddam's government periodically arrested and tortured him, rendering him unemployable. He fled to the anonymity of Baghdad where—in a house without electricity and very often no food—he sheltered his wife and children in the city's slums while occasionally obtaining work as a tailor.

When the Iraqi government formed the Ministry of the Environment in 2003, Ibrahem eagerly volunteered his talents. He created the Department of Marshes within the Ministry and still finds the time to consult with Nature Iraq and oversee the KBA field work.

THREATENED SPECIES IN THE MARSHES

Ibrahem speaks of the fish in Iraq as if they were friends—friends that he likes to eat. "The first species in southern Iraq, the one that everyone remembers with sadness, is *gattan* (*Luciobarbus xanthopterus*, formerly known as *Barbus xanthopterus*). *Gattan* are white-fleshed, oily fish that are very tasty for eating. It is an indigenous species and the people especially like it. They will pay eight dollars a pound

(0.4 kg) for *gattan*, compared to about two to five dollars a pound for any other fish. *Gattan* live in both the Tigris and the Euphrates rivers. They make their nests and lay their eggs within the rocky stream beds, so they need to go far upstream near Samarra where the rivers have some rocky beds; they can't spawn down here in the south because the riverbeds are all soft mud. After the eggs hatch, the larvae migrate down to the marshes, but because of the dams and barrages that have been constructed on these rivers, the path of migration has been cut off. It is therefore rare to see the *gattan* in southern Iraq now, except for a few small areas like Abu Zirig marsh and in the Shatt al-Arab River. You can imagine my delight when I found it in northern Iraq. It is very abundant in Tharthar Lake, especially because the violence there keeps the fishermen away."

The giant *bizz* (*Luciobarbus esocinus*, formerly known as *Barbus esocinus*), also known as the mangar or Tigris Salmon (although it is not a salmon), is another species that previously occurred in the marshlands but has not yet returned in large numbers since its restoration, although it has been found in Abu Zirig Marsh and the Shatt al-Arab. Saddam used to stock *bizz*, which can weigh up to 300 lbs, in the artificial lakes surrounding one of his palaces in Baghdad, and U.S. servicemen and women stationed there angled for his prizes.

When Lieutenant Colonel Joel Stewart packed for his mission to Iraq in 2005, as a last-moment impulse he threw in his rod and reel: *fishing in Iraq could be cool*, he thought. As he discovered, the fishing at Saddam's palace was outstanding, and he started the Baghdad Angling Club and Fly Fishing School to help provide recreation to the soldiers on duty there. Their website displays photographs of their captures: the winner so far is a five-foot (1.5 m), 100-pound (45 kg) behemoth *bizz* brought in on bagel bait. The magnificent catch fought for an hour, breaking the line six times and the rod once.

Another important native species of fish now only rarely found in the marshes is the *shabout* (*Tor grypus*, formerly known as *Barbus grypus*), one of the best fish for cooking over open flames in the local method known as *masgouf*. Several kinds of fish can be used, but *shabout* is the preferred variety for this style of barbecue. The fish is kept alive until the fire is ready, then it is split down the back, butterflied, impaled on sticks and set on the downwind side of the fire with the inside of the fish facing the fire so as to achieve a rich, smoky aroma. During the hour it takes to cook, the oils of the fish will seep through its flesh as a marinade. At the end of this roasting, the fish is placed directly on the embers to achieve a crispy skin. The first recipe for *masgouf* was found in ancient Sumerian texts, which describe a method of cooking fish by having it first "touched by fire" and then "placed on fire." During times of peace, moonlit nights in the summertime would find the banks of the Tigris in Baghdad filled with picnickers making campfires to prepare *masgouf.*

When the KBA surveys first started, *shabout* were nowhere to be found in the southern marshes, and the locals were preparing *masgouf* with Common Carp (an exotic). When the KBA surveys began in the north, they found the tasty fish in Razzaza, Derbendikhan and Dokan Lakes in northern Iraq. Finally Ibrahem found *shabout* in the south. Strangely enough, it hadn't migrated from northern Iraq.

"In 2006, we were sampling in the Shatt al-Arab and we caught some *shabout*, and I wondered where they could come from, how they got here from northern Iraq?" he recalls asking. "Then I realized that the Shatt al-Arab is also connected with the Karun River coming from Iran, so I looked up the fish and found that *shabout* is very common in the Karun River. I was hoping that maybe it could migrate back up into the marshes from Iran. Imagine my surprise when a year later we started to find *shabout* in Hammar Marsh, and then six months later we found them in Abu Zirig. I am so happy that these great fish have come back to us."

ENVIRONMENTAL CONSTRAINTS ON FISH POPULATIONS

But *shabout* will only struggle in the marshlands until environmental conditions are improved. The difficulty with sustaining their populations lies in the inability of many of the indigenous fish to tolerate the low oxygen conditions that frequently occur in the marshlands today, turning the water black and malodorous. To serve as a healthy environment for native fish, the dissolved oxygen levels should be higher than 5 mg/L (milligrams of oxygen per liter of water), but sometimes they sink below 2 mg/L—or even lower.

"One time I was measuring the oxygen level in Chubayish marshlands, I stayed overnight to see the daily change," Ibrahem explains. "When the sun goes down, photosynthesis (which produces oxygen) stops and chemosynthesis and respiration (which use up oxygen) dominate. Just before dawn, the oxygen content reached zero."

The marshes receiving water from the Euphrates exhibit particularly low dissolved oxygen concentrations. Sewage is disposed directly into the river as it crosses Syria and Iraq. As the water passes through the mid-Euphrates region it is used to cultivate rice, further degrading its quality. By the time the river reaches Nasriya, its water is old, hard, and contaminated with insecticides and fertilizers. Therefore, when the water enters the marshes it produces an algal bloom. More algae grow than can be eaten by the herbivores, and the dead algae accumulate on the bottom where bacterial decay begins the natural breakdown process. The resulting bacterial respiration further removes oxygen from the water. Scientists term this sequence of events eutrophication.

Eutrophication is a particular problem in the Chubayish marshlands. Its water originates from the Euphrates, flowing very slowly northward across the marshlands until it reaches the same elevation as water levels in the Euphrates, and then stops. As a result, the northernmost portion of the Chubayish marshlands contains the most stagnant water, so it experiences very low oxygen concentrations. Fish kills frequently occur, particularly during the low-flow periods of summer and fall.

"One time the people of Chubayish called and told me that there had been a mass death of fish in their marshes," Ibrahem tells me. "When I asked them which fish was the first to die, they told me the *shillik (Aspius vorax)* and I knew that it would be the first because it has the smallest gill-raker area, so it is very sensitive to low oxygen."

RESTOCKING THE NATIVE FISH

Bunni (Mesopotamichthys sharpeyi, formerly known as *Barbus sharpeyi)* is another economically important native species that is somewhat less sensitive to low oxygen conditions than *gattan* and *shabout*, although it still requires good oxygenation. *Bunni* is the only one of the economically important native fish that actually spawns in the marshes. In the southern marshes, *bunni* was also a favorite fish to prepare in the *masgouf* style, but when the marshes were dried they disappeared. In 2004, USAID gave a small grant to the Marine Science Center at the University of Basra to develop a fish hatchery for *bunni*, so that small fish, called fingerlings, could be released back into the marshes to support the recovery of this native fish population. But making the hatchery a success meant overcoming many technical challenges.

First, the scientists had to collect and maintain suitable female *bunni* to produce eggs. The next challenge was to develop protocols to induce spawning under the conditions of the university's fish ponds in Basra, which of course differ in many respects from their native habitat. Then the scientists artificially fertilized the females' eggs and incubated the fertilized ova. After hatching, they reared the larva until they grew to the fingerling stage, when they could be released into the wild. The experiment was a success; now *bunni* that are more than six inches (15 cm) long can be found in East Hammar and Hawizeh marshes. Much more work must be undertaken, however, to restore a normal stock of *bunni* to the marshlands.

RETURN OF THE MIGRANTS

Beyond sheltering the freshwater fish of Iraq, the marshes also represent an essential habitat for anadromous fish—those that spend their adult lives in the ocean but are spawned and reared in freshwater ecosystems. In Iraq, one of the most important of these is the Hilsa or Indian Shad *(Tenualosa ilisha)*, known locally as *sbour*. These fish are extremely delectable but full of tiny bones; eating them requires a great amount of *sabr*—the Arabic word for patience. *Sbour* spend most of their lives in the northwestern Indian Ocean and the Gulf, but in the spring the shad migrate up the Shatt al-Arab into the marshes and the Euphrates and Tigris to spawn. Ecologists liken the marshes to a nursery that sustains and protects the vulnerable juveniles until the floods flush them back out to the ocean. Drying the marshes greatly decreased the habitat available for the shad's spawning, and the FAO estimates that the population of anadromous fish in the Gulf may have diminished by 50% during this time period.

When the eastern Hammar Marsh was re-flooded, no one knew if the anadromous fish would ever find their way back upstream to their old nursery. The marshes had been dry for a decade; only the very oldest of fish may have retained a memory of the place. But nature must have designed some impetus for the fish to search for the nursery, perhaps in the form of a chemical marker emanating from the marshes that the organisms can detect and follow. Indeed, they found their ancient pathway, and *sbour* are now abundant in eastern Hammar Marsh.

Another important visitor from the Gulf is a species of shrimp *(Metapenaeus affinis)* that spawns in the Gulf but grows to maturity in the wetlands. The shrimp (in larvae or post-larvae form) work their way up to the marshes, then the maturing juveniles migrate back out to sea. Although some Islamic sects believe that shrimp are not *halal* (acceptable) food, an artisanal shrimp fishery thrives in both the waters of Iraq and the Gulf.

In addition to fish and shrimp, the Bull Shark *(Carcharhinus leucas)* was a common visitor from the Gulf to the Shatt al-Arab and the lower reaches of the Tigris and Euphrates rivers, and Wilfred Thesiger reported that small sharks made infrequent incursions into the marshlands. Even this somewhat unwelcome fish has once again returned to southern Iraq, observed recently in the waters of the Main Outfall Drain.

FOREIGN INVASIONS

Re-flooding the marshes allowed for the resurgence of several native species but also created a hospitable environment for some foreign species of fish that had previously been introduced to Iraqi waters. Some introductions have been accidental. For example, fish farms in Iraq typically raise species such as the Common Carp *(Cyprinus carpio)*. The fish can escape from their ponds during floods and, in the natural environment, begin to dominate the habitat. These omnivorous carp eat anything available, thereby competing in the food chain with almost every other fish. They grow rapidly and tolerate low-oxygen conditions better than most native species; their actions tend to increase turbidity and disrupt natural habitat. Now non-native carp are the most abundant fish in the marshes. Additionally, the ornamental Common Goldfish *(Carassius auratus)* escaped from private aquaria in Iraq and, after reverting to a more natural olive-brown, are also very abundant in the re-flooded marshes.

The Stinging Catfish *(Heteropneustes fossilis)* was introduced to Iraq's lakes in the 1950s, supposedly because they eat mosquito larvae. Unfortunately, the fish migrated into all of Iraq's waters, where they pose an increasing danger to fishermen. However,

Ibrahem is most worried by another species of catfish known locally as *jirri (Silurius triostegus).*

"There are a lot of *jirri* in the marshes," he says, "but the Shia Muslims [the dominant sect in the marshlands] never eat catfish. We say it is *haram* in Islam because it doesn't have scales to protect the body, so when the fishermen catch them they release them again. However, the *jirri* is a major carnivore in the marshes. It eats the juveniles of the other fish, decreasing the population of the economically important fish, which are mostly herbivores or omnivores. Because the fishermen don't catch the *jirri*, we find that the fish population is dominated by these carnivores. That's upside down: in a healthy ecosystem we should see more herbivores than carnivores. Now we have lots of *jirri* eating the small fish that could grow up to be good food for the fishermen."

"So I am thinking how we can get rid of the *jirri*," he goes on. "I proposed a project that we could use these fish that are *haram*, we could make a fish food factory, catch these fish and dry them and make pellets. They have a good concentration of animal proteins and it is very good as feed for either fish farms or for chicken. This way, we can use the fish and regain the balance in the food-pyramid. I told the Ministry of Agriculture about this idea, and they now have a pilot project in Hawizeh Marsh. I have optimism that it will work and we can copy this example for other marsh areas."

HUMAN IMPACT ON FISH POPULATIONS

In addition to environmental threats, some of the fishing practices used by the local people also pose a danger to the survival of the native fish population. Poison fishing has been a long-standing problem in the marshes; in the 1950s Thesiger described the common practice of using *datura* (a natural poison made from jimsonweed) to temporarily stun the fish, enabling their easy capture. *Datura*, however, killed only the fish that ate the poison pellets. Now some people spread long-acting insecticides and herbicides over the water to kill the fish, and unknowingly they kill everything in the water.

The former Iraqi government repressed Ibrahem's desire to rid the marshes of poison fishing. Now he is free to lobby against the destructive practice. Nature Iraq has had success in some of the marshes by asking the local religious leaders to make a prohibition against fishing by poison and electricity, to issue what is known as a *fatwa* against harmful fishing methods. The leaders agreed, and even Grand Ayatollah Sayyid Ali al-Sistani issued a *fatwa* against poison fishing. Flags to remind the marsh dwellers of the prohibition have been placed throughout the Chubayish marshes. The *fatwa* worked well in some areas; in the Abu Zirig marshes, for example, everyone now fishes by legal methods. In some remote areas, however, poison fishing continues.

Electro-fishing remains common in the marshlands. In this method, a small portable generator, carried in the *mashuf,* is connected to an electrode on the end of a pole. An electrical current is generated, and subsequently the fisherman uses a hand-net to scoop up the stunned fish. Theoretically, only the larger fish are affected and the smaller fish can move away, but the crude devices used in Iraq may create stronger electrical fields than recommended for sustainable yields. The electricity doesn't linger in the environment like poison, but there is concern that repeated stresses due to daily usage of electricity could have long-term impacts on the reproductive success of the fishes.

To deter these harmful practices, the Ministry of Environment is contemplating the development of an environmental police force similar to Fish & Game wardens in other countries. But people need to eat and they must feed their families. Therefore, after much deliberation, Nature Iraq decided the best way to discourage these damaging methods was to offer alternative forms of obtaining fish that provide a more sustainable livelihood. In 2006, Ibrahem read about the concept of floating fish farms—essentially nets suspended in natural waters to raise fish in captivity—and he developed the concept for Nature Iraq with his colleagues at the University of Basra.

Each floating fish farm consists of a large net suspended beneath a 20- by 30-foot (6 by 9 m) frame constructed from 8-inch-diameter (20 cm) foam-filled plastic pipes. The floating farm is best placed in the flowing river environment to reduce the possibility of stagnation. Fingerlings are introduced, raised to maturity and then harvested as desired. The fish can feed on whatever is floating through the water, but additional fish feed is usually beneficial to improve survival and achieve the maximum growth rate.

Nature Iraq installed a prototype on the Euphrates River to test the practicality and effectiveness of the methodology and determine whether any adverse effects on the surrounding water quality and ecosystem occurred. The experiment worked extremely well. Local fishermen, observing the prototype floating fish farm, are eager to create their own. The team wants to learn how to make the frame out of bundles of reeds that will float on their own, so the locals will be able to construct the farms themselves.

THE CURRENT TALLY

The KBA surveys have shown that the restored marshes are capable of supporting healthy populations of native fish, if proper conservation methods are emplaced to ensure a sustainable fishery. So far, the areas exhibiting the highest biodiversity are the eastern Hammar marshes, where the mix of freshwater and marine fish boosts the species count to 15, including the economically-important fish *gattan, bunni* and *sbour*. Abu Zirig marsh also has healthy populations of fish: the maximum species count here is 13, dominated by non-native carp but including the highly-valued native fish *gattan* and *bizz*. A maximum of 13 species have also been observed in Hawizeh marsh, including the economically-important native species *gattan* and *bunni*. The Shatt al-Arab, though not a marshland, has also been found to support a large diversity of fish, including 13 freshwater and 31 marine species, including *bizz, sbour,* and *shabout*.

Statistics on the Iraqi inland fish capture demonstrate the value of ecosystem restoration to the food supply of the country. The annual catch averaged around 17,000 tons (15,000 metric tons) during the 1970s and 1980s, and briefly climbed to around 22,000 tons (20,000 metric tons) during the mid-1990s as the marshes dried and the decreasing aquatic acreage concentrated the fish allowing for easier capture. After the marshes disappeared altogether, the average annual catch of freshwater fish declined to 11,000 tons (10,000 metric tons) between 1998 and 2004. As the wetlands were re-flooded, the catch rose to 25,000 tons (23,000 metric tons) in 2005 and then to 50,000 tons (45,000 metric tons) in 2006 and 2007. Aquaculture also improved during this time period; by 2003, fish farm production had been reduced to 2,200 tons (2,000 metric tons) but rose to 17,000 tons (15,000 metric tons) in 2006.

"My greatest hope for the marshlands," Ibrahem concludes, "my goal for all of the work, is to see Iraq preserve the treasure of its fish. We gain a lot of good from the fish, and I want to help the fishermen learn how to use this treasure sustainably, so that we will always have them for our future."

10. GETTING THE WATER RIGHT

"And the Lord God planted a garden in Eden, and there he put the man that
he had formed. And out of the ground the Lord God made to grow every
tree that is pleasant to the sight and good for food, the tree of life also in the
midst of the garden, and the tree of the knowledge of good and evil. A river
flowed out of Eden to water the garden, and there it divided and became
four rivers. The name of the first is Pishon … the name of the second river
is Gihon … the name of the third river is the Tigris … and the fourth river
is the Euphrates."

—Genesis 2 (8-14) the Holy Bible, Revised Standard Version

Every now and then, dark clouds gather over southern Iraq and a
few drops of rain fall onto its thirsty soil. But precipitation in this
arid region averages only six inches (15 cm) per year, and the climate
is so hot (the average high August is 108°F or 42°C) that the air is
capable of evaporating well over 100 inches (250 cm) of rain each
year. Clearly, these marshes depend completely on water from the
two great rivers of the region—the Tigris and Euphrates. And within
Iraq, all of that enormous stream flow is controlled by its Ministry of
Water Resources. The fate of the marshlands is truly in their hands.

Irrigation was invented in Iraq, and its ancient ruler Hammurabi
encoded the world's first water regulations; this country should be
eminently capable of rational and just distribution of this precious
resource. During the 1950s and 1960s, Iraq's Ministry of Irrigation
was well regarded throughout the Middle East, but Saddam Hussein
diverted control of the ministry from its technical experts to his
loyal Ba'ath party members, who subsequently ran the ministry like a
police bureau. The Iraqi Intelligence Service (a Ba'ath version of the
Nazi's Gestapo) even constructed a branch office in the ministry's
basement, including a prison and torture chamber.

Under Saddam's rule, the institution's mission gradually transformed from beneficial to malevolent as he ordered its engineers to develop plans to desiccate the southern marshlands. The ministry suffered further as the UN-imposed economic sanctions, intended to punish Saddam in the aftermath of the Gulf War, deteriorated the ministry's resources to such a degree that critical pumping stations and massive dams stood on the brink of failure. The recent war inflicted even more direct structural damage to the country's water supply system. When Saddam's government finally fell, the ministry's headquarters in Baghdad was destroyed by fire and over $100 million in capital assets were lost during the weeks of looting that ensued.

REBUILDING THE MINISTRY

Fast on the heels of the combat troops came the professionals of the U.S. Army Corps of Engineers, who took immediate control of the ministry's assets and successfully managed its water flow without incident. Dr. Eugene Stakhiv served as the ministry's first Senior Advisor, subsequent advisors including Jerry Webb, Darryl Davis, and Dr. Edwin Theriot. With Corps assistance, the ministry began to move beyond simple control of irrigation into a comprehensive water management role. In May 2004, Water Resources was the first Iraqi ministry to regain sovereignty and begin to function independently of the CPA, under the leadership of Dr. Abdul Latif Rashid. Dr. Rashid was succeeded by Engineer Mohaned al-Saadi in 2010.

Iraq's fledgling Ministry of Water Resources inherited an enormous and crumbling water resources infrastructure. Minister Rashid immediately embarked upon an ambitious plan to modernize the ministry. He increased its funding from a few million to $500 million and used the money for desperately needed repair and maintenance of irrigation works, and began to implement management of the water system with new technology. By 2008, the ministry employed about 35,000 people throughout the country and had over a thousand ongoing field activities.

Although the ministry controls the flow of water within Iraq, their efforts are completely dependent on how much water is released into Iraq by its upstream neighbors, and therein lies the crux of Iraq's water problem: most of it originates outside the country. The marshlands, lying at the farthest downstream end of the rivers, rely not only upon the goodwill of the Iraqi government, but upon the governments of Turkey, Syria, and Iran as well.

THE EUPHRATES RIVER

The Euphrates feeds both the Central and Hammar Marshes. This mighty river gains the majority of its water at its origin in Turkey and the remainder as it traverses Syria. Historically, the Euphrates brought about 30 billion cubic meters (bcm)[10] into Iraq, but floods could double that amount and a drought could halve it. During the early part of the 20th century, Iraq often experienced an influx of too much water, and many of its earliest water control structures were designed to avert devastating floods. But the situation began to alter dramatically during the 1970s.

Syria began the race to control the Euphrates in 1973 with the construction of the Tabqa Dam, having a reservoir with a potential capacity of 12 bcm; a year later Turkey completed the huge Keban Dam with a reservoir capacity of 31 bcm. During the 1980s, both Iraq and Turkey completed several smaller dams, but all of these structures were dwarfed by Turkey's erection of the gigantic Ataturk Dam, having a reservoir capacity of 49 bcm. Taken together, the reservoirs behind Turkey's existing dams on the Euphrates have the capacity to retain several years' worth of its average flow without letting any water pass beyond its border. These dams essentially give Turkey's politicians the power to unilaterally reduce the flow of the mighty river—the largest in southwest Asia—to a trickle.

And they have. In 1990, while the reservoir behind the recently-completed Ataturk Dam filled, the riverbed of the Euphrates River in southern Iraq literally dried up. After the reservoir reached its capacity, Turkey resumed its release of water downstream of the dam, yet after 1990 the amount of water flowing through the Euphrates into Iraq had been reduced by one-third to around 19 bcm.

The Ataturk Dam represents one of the largest components of Turkey's Southeast Anatolian Project (commonly referred to as the GAP project). This massive program—expected to cost more than $30 billion—envisages a string of 22 dams on the Euphrates and Tigris Rivers. About half of the proposed dams have been completed; most of these have been constructed for the main purpose of hydropower generation. To generate electricity, water must be released through the

---

[10] A billion cubic meters is equivalent to 1.3 billion cubic yards or 250 billion gallons or 810,000 acre-feet; as bcm is the standard scientific unit no English equivalents are provided in the text.

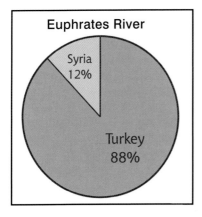
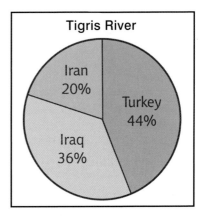

Figure 6. Water Sources of the Euphrates and Tigris Rivers

dam, and therefore the completed component of the project does not impact the water quantity flowing downstream as greatly as its irrigation component will. Construction of the irrigation works has only begun, and their completion will not only further reduce the amount of water flowing out of Turkey but also will significantly deteriorate its quality, as spent irrigation water, filled with salts, fertilizers, pesticides and herbicides, will be drained back into the rivers.

Turkey is not alone in its wish to increase its agricultural production. Syria also has plans to double the area within its country that is irrigated from the Euphrates, increasing its net diversions from 5 bcm to 10 bcm. At full development, and unless some sort of water sharing agreement is put into place, the Turkish and Syrian projects could reduce Iraq's share of the Euphrates to 6 bcm, and even less in a drought year. For example, during the drought of 2009 only 9 bcm flowed through this river into Iraq. With only a slow trickle of water flowing into Iraq, it is certain that very little would remain by the time the rivers reached the southern marshlands.

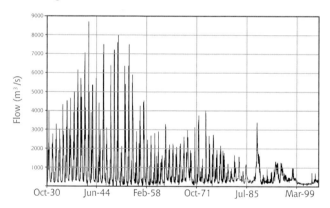

Figure 7. Flows of the Euphrates and Tigris Rivers Inside Iraq

THE TIGRIS RIVER

The Tigris supplies water to both the Central and Hawizeh Marshes. This river collects about half of its flow in Turkey and half within Iraq and Iran from tributaries including the Greater Zab, Lesser Zab, Adheim and Diyala Rivers, all of which originate in the Zagros Mountains along the border between Iraq and Iran. Iran controls the headwaters of several of the tributaries to the Tigris, including the Diyala and the Lesser Zab Rivers. Historically, the Tigris carried an average of 22 bcm annually into Iraq, and its tributaries within Iraq contributed an additional 28 bcm. Iraq has constructed a number of water-control structures on the Tigris and its tributaries for flood control, irrigation, and hydropower generation.

Neither Turkey nor Syria has yet constructed large dams on the Tigris, and as a result water flow and water quality are currently far superior to that of the Euphrates. On the Tigris, the largest structure proposed under Turkey's GAP project is the Ilısu Dam, with a reservoir designed to hold about half of the river's annual flow in Turkey. Construction of the Ilisu Dam began in 2006 and is anticipated to be completed by 2015.

The Ilisu is primarily intended for hydropower generation, which would necessitate the release of water through the dam. However, Turkey also plans to construct a smaller structure—the Cizre Dam—immediately downstream of the Ilisu Dam. The Cizre Dam is intended to intercept the water released from the Ilisu Dam and divert it for irrigation projects. Clearly, construction of the Ilisu and Cizre Dams poses a significant threat to Iraq's water security and to the survival of its southern marshlands.

THE KARKHEH AND KARUN RIVERS

As the Tigris and Euphrates flow towards the marshes, they divide into distributaries that feed into the vast wetlands. At Qurna, the two rivers merge into one, known as the Shatt al-Arab, which flows past the city of Basra and into the Gulf. Sovereignty of the Shatt al-Arab has long been a source of controversy between Iran and Iraq, forming one of the reasons for the Iran-Iran war. South of Basra, the thalweg or centerline of the Shatt al-Arab represents the international boundary between the two countries.

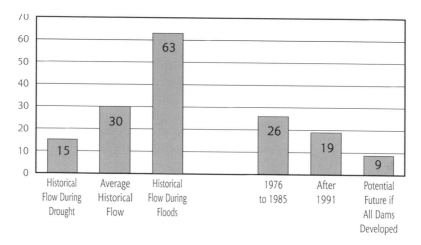

Figure 8. Flow of the Euphrates River into Iraq (bcm)

The Karun River, the largest in Iran, carries an annual flow of about 24 bcm. As it nears the coast, the river breaks into two distributaries— before 2009, about 14 bcm flowed through the Haffar Canal into the Shatt al-Arab near the Iranian city of Khorramshahr, while the remainder flowed through the Bahmanshir River, paralleling the Shatt al-Arab, and discharging directly into the Gulf. The flow of the Karun into the Shatt al-Arab maintained its freshwater nature and kept the saltwater of the Gulf from backing up into its estuary. Migratory fish and other aquatic life within the rivers and Gulf depend on the fresh water in the Shatt al-Arab; saltwater intrusion could devastate the local fisheries.

In 2009, Iran blocked the flow of the Karun through the Haffar and saltwater crept far upstream into the Shatt al-Arab estuary, depriving many municipalities of a source of fresh drinking water and causing the closure of several electrical power plants; three Basra provinces were declared disaster areas. Now all of the flow of the

Karun streams through the Bahmanshir into the Gulf. The long-term impacts of this action on the ecology of the Shatt al-Arab and the Gulf have not yet been studied.

The Karkheh River is one of the largest in Iran and possesses water of such rare sweetness that the ancient kings of Persia declared the river sacred. The river originates in the highlands of the Zagros Mountains, wends its way gradually south, then turns west and finally debouches into the wetlands known in Iran as the Azim Marsh and in Iraq as the Hawizeh Marsh. The marsh dwellers seldom respected this artificial boundary, and the natural system functioned as a single unit. Around 6 bcm from the Karkheh historically crossed the swampy border into Iraq. During the early 2000s, it was this influx that kept Hawizeh alive while the Ba'ath regime struggled to dry the marshlands. The flow reduced dramatically after Iran erected the Karkheh Dam in 2002. Then Iran began constructing an earthen dyke along its border with Iraq in 2004, effectively creating two separate marshes; at the present time, no flow from the Karkheh reaches Hawizeh Marsh.

WATER-SHARING AGREEMENTS

For the last four decades, Iraq's upstream neighbors have been gradually decreasing the flow of water across their borders. Clearly these countries must establish agreements to equitably share this precious resource or Iraq will slowly die of dehydration. Much of Iraq's historical water supply originates in Turkey, yet no water resources treaty exists between the two countries.

During construction of the Ataturk Dam, Turkey unilaterally promised to maintain a flow of 16 bcm in the Euphrates River across its border into Syria. Syria and Iraq have agreed that Syria would pass 58% of this amount on to Iraq. But under these conditions, Iraq would receive less than a third of its historical share of the Euphrates' water. The marshlands, at the far downstream end of the system, could once again disappear.

No treaty has been established for the Tigris River, which remains largely uncontrolled by dams upstream of Iraq. It is critically important that Iraq and Turkey sign a water sharing treaty before construction of the Ilisu and Cizre dams is complete. Likewise, Iraq lacks a water treaty with Iran for sharing the flows of the Tigris tributaries that headwater in Iran, or for the Karkheh or Karun Rivers.

Clearly the new government of Iraq has a lot of work to do, but it remains hampered by instability and political infighting. Not much progress has been made beyond the re-establishment of a Joint Technical Committee between Turkey, Syria, and Iraq in 2008 to share water data and cooperatively study water resources issues facing the three nations.

Iraq must also learn to make better use of its ever-decreasing water resources, but conservation will require a difficult metamorphosis of the Iraqi mentality. Most of the wheat, barley and rice fields of central Iraq are still cultivated by flood irrigation, a method inherited from the ancient Sumerians. Beyond wasting huge amounts of water, the practice eventually leads to the accumulation of salts in the soil, rendering the land unusable. Although they involve a significant up-front capital investment, sprinkler systems are much better suited to field agriculture in an arid environment. Drip irrigation, now virtually unknown in Iraq, could also be implemented for fruit and vegetable production.

THE CENTER FOR RESTORATION OF THE IRAQI MARSHLANDS

Traditionally, the MoWR has focused on delivering water to the agricultural, urban, and energy sectors: allocating water to the environment represents a rather new concept. Within the ministry, the driving force for environmental restoration is the Center for Restoration of the Iraqi Marshlands (CRIM), and the driving force behind the creation of CRIM was Dr. Hassan Janabi.

"My main passion in life is the marshes," Janabi muses. "I think they have taken my life over: thinking marshes, doing marshes, talking about marshes. When I was young I would spend my holidays with my family near the seasonal marshes of Najaf. At that age I saw the marsh as big as the sea. When we got to our village, we had to get out of the car and walk in the reeds to get to my auntie's house. I can still remember feeling a great sense of excitement and freedom that I was entering a different world … when I was about 10 years old I was very fond of a little girl from the village. It was just an innocent affection, but I would long for the holiday to go and see her. I remember seeing her paddle her *mashuf* along, and sometimes in the late afternoon when she came back home from working in the marshes, she would sing …"

Hassan pauses with a faraway look in his eyes.

After being arrested and tortured by the Ba'ath regime, Janabi fled the country and ended up in Australia, where he studied and later worked in the Sydney Water Corporation and then the Sydney Catchment Authority. But he never forgot about the marshlands. In February 2003 he was offered a job with ORHA as an advisor to the fledgling Ministry of Water Resources.

Hassan readily perceived that the ministry's focus on irrigation would mean that little attention would be paid to the environment. He therefore decided that the ministry needed a formal group that could devote all its effort to restoring the marshlands. So in the fall of 2003, he founded CRIM. Jassim Asadi immediately volunteered to work for the group, and Janabi recognized untapped talent in two female engineers who agreed to join him—Samira Shabeeb and Ekram Qassim.

"They were very committed to the marshlands, but they needed a lot of education," Janabi explained. "It was just the five of us in an office within the ministry, and we had no real power to implement projects, but I think that we did a lot of good—we educated a lot of people. Through CRIM we were able to coordinate all the various projects—USAID, Iraq Foundation, Nature Iraq, IMELS, and the other Iraqi ministries. We held a lot of very good, high-profile meetings with all of the ministries."

Janabi left his family in March 2003 against the vigorous objections of his wife, who had just broken her hand and strongly opposed becoming a virtual single parent. He did not see them again until August 2004, when he convinced them to return to Iraq with him. The family drove from Jordan to Baghdad full of hope for a bright future together. But as they passed near Fallujah, highwaymen attacked their car, jabbing an AK-47 into his older son's throat and demanding their valuables: $20,000 cash, his wife's wedding ring, and his younger son's new Discman. They lost everything, but nevertheless they felt lucky; if the robbers had known about Janabi's duties in Baghdad, he may have been kidnapped and beheaded. Needless to say, his family returned to Australia while Janabi continued as an advisor to the Ministry of Water Resources. In 2008 he was appointed Iraq's ambassador to UN-FAO, and he and his wife and younger son were finally able to live together in Rome.

In 2008, Abdul Kadhum Lahmoud became the Director of CRIM, which now operates with increased funding, manpower, and authority to implement projects. He is a civil engineer by training, and one of the best in the country, but he thinks like an ecologist. An expansive and genial man, Lahmoud believes he has spent his whole life preparing for this work.

"This is the fifth General Directorate that I have been assigned," Lahmoud declares. "I have directed the survey department, the river department, the department of land reclamation, and I also served as director of all of the ministry's governmental companies. And now I find that this job requires all of this experience, all of the skills that I have learned are now applied to this problem of restoring the marshes."

"To provide for the needs of the marshes, we have to prove their usefulness from all aspects, both biodiversity and economy, locally and regionally. You know we have fish that live in the northern Gulf and migrate all the way to Indonesia, birds that migrate from the marshes north to Siberia and south to Africa. The Tigris and Euphrates, like any rivers, gradually become more and more polluted as they flow along—the tail end of any river is not pure water. But the marshes act as a filter for this water. Without the marshes, all of this polluted water ends up in the Gulf and eventually ends up in the fish. So the restoration of the marshes is not only an Iraqi need but it is an international need. This is the argument I use to ask the neighboring countries to make special considerations for the marshes, to allocate water resources to them so that we can maintain these marshes that affect the rest of the world."

Lahmoud is a practical man of action, well respected within the ministry, and as a result he was able to transform CRIM from a five-person operation working in one cramped office to a full General Directorate with its own building and dozens of employees.

With the help of international donors, the team has grown in technical sophistication. USAID supplied the group with new technology, including field equipment, computers, software, and laboratory apparatus. UNEP, with funding from JICA and IMELS, developed the Marshlands Information Network, an internet data-sharing resource, which was then turned over to CRIM. In 2006, CRIM took over UNEP's satellite monitoring program. Nature Iraq and the Italian experts have continued to support CRIM with various studies, ad hoc evaluations, and quick designs. CRIM now functions as the front-line government office for marshland restoration.

THE NEW EDEN MASTER PLAN FOR THE MARSHLANDS

In 2005, Nature Iraq, CRIM, and Italian experts began a collaboration to prepare the "New Eden Master Plan for Integrated Water Resources Management in the Marshlands Area" with financial sponsorship by IMELS. The New Eden team is headed by Nature Iraq and involves 70 Iraqi and 45 Italian engineers and scientists and experts from the U.S. Army Corps of Engineers Hydraulic Engineering Center, the U.S. Geological Survey, and UNEP, working over a two–year period to prepare the 1,600 pages of documentation. Andrea Cattarossi, who has dedicated many years of his career to restoring Iraq's marshes, led the project.

After finalizing extensive analyses, the Master Plan concluded that 75% of the former marshlands area was both available and desirable for restoration: that is, the dried marshlands had not been redeveloped for any other productive use, such as agricultural land or oilfields, and the local inhabitants wanted their marshlands restored. The results also demonstrated that the wise use of Iraq's water resources could allow for the restoration of 50-75% of the dried marshlands. The report therefore recommended that future efforts should focus on enhancing biodiversity and long-term environmental sustainability within those areas of the marshlands that had already been re-flooded by their local inhabitants.

OPTIMIZING MARSHLAND RESTORATION

Ecological evaluations by the KBA surveys concluded that the re-growth of native vegetation and the return of indigenous biodiversity had been limited by poor water quality, the lack of seasonality in water flow, and the absence of hydraulic and ecological connections between the rivers and the different wetland units.

Salinity and oxygen content are the most critical aspects of water quality in these marshlands. To maintain low salinity and high oxygen content, water within the marshes must be constantly replenished. In this arid climate, if water flows into the marshlands and simply stays in one place, evaporation will rapidly increase its salinity while respiration and decomposition of the abundant organic material will quickly deplete its oxygen. Therefore, water must keep moving through the marshes: both inflow and outflow must be maintained, or as the scientists put it, "hydraulic flow-through" must be achieved.

The seasonality of water quantity and quality is also vitally important for ecosystem health. Under natural conditions, springtime brought the annual floods that refreshed, deepened, and expanded the waters of the permanent marshes. During the heat of the summer, evaporation and outflow would decrease water levels and increase salinity in the wetlands while drying the seasonal fringe around the permanent marshes. This annual variation in water levels and quality would trigger key ecological processes such as germination and spawning; it enhances the decomposition of organic material and the recycling of nutrients. Scientists refer to these natural variations in the water level of the marsh as its "hydro-period": without these cyclical changes, the full character and biodiversity of the marshes cannot be restored.

Upstream dams not only decrease the quantity of water coming into Iraq but also disrupt its seasonal variations. The snowmelts of spring no longer produce floods and the seasonality of flow has been greatly dampened. Iraq cannot control the timing of water release from other countries' dams, but the New Eden team determined that an artificial hydro-period could be created in the marshes by managing the local flow of water through inlets and outlets of the wetlands.

To improve conditions in the Hawizeh Marsh, the New Eden engineers determined that flow regulators at its two outlets would enable the re-creation of an artificial flood pulse. The engineers also recommended removal of the dykes separating northern from southern Hawizeh to increase hydraulic flow-through and re-establish ecological corridors between the marsh units.

In the Central Marshes, the Master Plan suggested that the Iraqi government could divert one of the Tigris distributary channels—the Butaira—away from the Glory Canal and back along its historical course southward into the Chubayish marsh, thus greatly reducing the salinity and temperature of the water in the marshlands and potentially achieving hydraulic flow-through if sufficient quantities of water were available. The diversion of the Butaira could also create an ecological corridor between the Tigris and Euphrates ecosystems.

A flood pulse could also be created in the Central Marshes through the installation of regulators at their intersection with the Euphrates. The levees along the Euphrates have been breached at nine locations, and the channels at the breaches alter seasonally between inlets and outlets. When the water level in the Euphrates is high during the spring, water flows from the river into the marsh, but when the Euphrates is at a low stage in the late summer, water flows from the marsh into the river. Closing the regulators when the Euphrates is low would retain water in the marshes.

The western Hammar Marshes, traditionally supplied by the Euphrates River, also suffer from low water quantity and quality. To increase the water supply, the Master Plan recommends enlarging one of the inlets from the Euphrates and constructing a structure to capture the water flowing out from the Abu Zirig and direct it into the northwestern side of the Hammar Marsh.

The most critical problem in Hammar is the lack of a hydraulic connection between the eastern and western ends of the marshes. Historically functioning as one unit, the two sides have been cut off from each other by the dykes protecting the oilfields that run through the Hammar marshes. Currently, a raised roadway (the Aramco Bridge) runs from north to south joining the North and South Rumaila oilfields. The existing roadway contains culverts that should allow for water flow, but they are blocked by sediment. The Master Plan suggests the reconstruction of this embankment with larger culverts and water regulators underneath, to allow for a regulated flow of water between the two marsh units.

In total, the Master Plan recommends capital improvements valued at $25 million. After two years of review, the MoWR approved the Master Plan. CRIM initiated the projects in December 2008 and completed them in 2012.

11. LEGISLATING THE ENVIRONMENT

"I set out a great park... wherein were all kinds of herbs and fruit trees, trees such as grow on the mountains and in Chaldea ... I made a swamp and set out a cane-brake therein ... the cane-brakes developed rapidly; the birds of heaven, the iguru birds, built their nests, and the wild swine and beasts of the forests brought forth young in abundance. The mulberry and the cypress, the product of the parks, the reeds of the brakes which were in the swamp, I cut down and used them as desired, in the building of my royal palaces."

—Sennacherib Inscription at Ninevah (ca. 715 BC)

The warrior king Sennacherib, wishing to display the rich natural heritage of the southern marshes and northern mountains of his empire at his palace in Ninevah, constructed the world's first botanical and wildlife park more than 1,200 years ago on the plains of central Iraq. Now nature preserves and botanical parks are once again being planned in Iraq, in this instance by Iraq's Ministry of the Environment, led by Minister Narmin Othman from 2004 to 2010; and subsequently Minister Sargon Lazon Sliwah who continues her legacy of strong environmental activism

Othman is a Kurd from northern Iraq, and she has followed a long and tortuous path to reach her current standing as one of the most powerful women in Iraq. Although she lacks any formal training in environmental science, Othman has an extensive background in politics. But partisan debates in Baghdad seem trivial to her when she recollects the horrendous atrocities that she and her people have endured.

The Kurdish people are the world's largest minority that lacks a homeland. Ethnically, they are Indo-European, not Arab. For centuries they have experienced repression, and they remain scattered across northern Iraq, southeastern Turkey, northwestern

Iran, and Syria. Under the Ba'ath government they suffered as greatly as the people of the marshlands.

When the government in Baghdad began the campaign against its Kurdish population in 1974, Othman's husband decided to join the mountain guerilla group known as *peshmerga*—the word literally means "facing death"—fighting against Saddam's government forces. Eventually he was captured and incarcerated in the notorious Abu Ghraib prison where he was mercilessly tortured, including having his fingernails torn out. He was released from prison in 1979. Then, inexplicably, Narmin herself was arrested.

"They asked me why I wasn't helping the Ba'ath Party," she told me. "They said that if wasn't with them I was against them. Then they let me go and the next day we went to the mountains. I had to leave my young son with my mother, and I became a *peshmerga* with my husband."

The extent to which Othman may have engaged in armed combat during her time with the guerilla forces isn't clear; she maintains that her role was primarily political and educational. Words are her weapon of choice, but essays and treatises would have been powerless against the heavily-armed Republican Guard who hunted the rebels down. For five years she and her husband struggled to exist in the rugged mountain wilderness until they finally recognized they could no longer survive in Iraq. They sought political asylum in Sweden; again she was forced to leave her son behind with his grandmother. In 1990 her husband returned to Iraq and she joined him two years later.

Othman immediately set to work organizing humanitarian relief for the Kurdish refugees, and in 1999 she became Minister of Social Affairs, and subsequently Minister of Education, for the Kurdistan Regional Government. Then when the Ba'ath government fell in 2003, both she and her husband became active in national politics.

In March 2004 Othman's husband died after a brief illness. Two months later, bereft of her lifelong partner yet fiercely desiring to continue their life of public service, she joined Iraq's interim government as Minister of Women's Affairs. Then the elected government asked her to serve as both Minister of Environment and Minister of Human Rights. Under the Maliki government she was asked to retain the environmental portfolio.

Othman came to her love of the environment through her years spent as a freedom fighter in the mountains of northern Iraq. "There are two places in Iraq where you are speaking with God—the high places in the mountains and the marshlands. When I was *peshmerga*, alone in the mountains, I took my strength from nature, from the grasses and flowers and trees, from the waterfalls and rivers. The same pieces of water that come from our mountains, they end up in the marshes, and they are a gift given to Iraq."

Attempts on her life have not deterred her from her work; she shrugs off danger because throughout her life, everyone she cares for has always been at risk. "When I travel it's always with security, every car that passes, you think it's going to be a terrorist to kill you. Three times someone has tried to assassinate me. Two were big explosions from land mines, but I have an armored car, I was not seriously injured. In August 2005, I was traveling back to Baghdad from Sulaymania; terrorists attacked my convoy from every side. My bodyguards got out and returned fire; some of them were injured, but they fought off the attackers. Of course they are *peshmerga*. I have had them as my guards for a long time, some of them from 1992. I think they would die for me."

Under Ba'ath rule, environmental protection was only a minor department within Iraq's Ministry of Health; the Ministry of Environment was created by the new Constitution in 2004. Its first minister, a young law professor, fled to the United States in 2005 after receiving assassination threats. Othman inherited a skeleton staff lacking skills, infrastructure, equipment or even a clear set of goals. To build the organization, she had to beg, borrow, and steal personnel from other government ministries, from academia, and from every aid agency she encountered. Eventually she assembled a cadre of scientists, engineers and other specialists eager to work toward protecting Iraq's environment.

Othman's Deputy Minister for Technical Affairs was Dr. Kamal Hussein, who has taken a rather unusual path toward environmental conservation. After he graduated with a Ph.D. in physics from the University of Baghdad, Dr. Kamal initially pursued biophysical research but soon was sent to work in the Iraqi Atomic Energy Commission (IAEC), where he was asked to develop a set of highly sophisticated laser isotope separation techniques, with the ultimate goal of building a nuclear bomb. After the IAEC was disbanded in 2003, Kamal sought a position with the fledgling Ministry of Environment, eager to apply his scientific abilities to more peaceful projects.

But the ministry's staff has found it difficult to concentrate on environmental issues during the chaos of an unannounced civil war. "It is hard for my staff to even drive across the city to get to work," Othman said in 2006, when terrorism in Baghdad was killing over

2,000 people per month. "There are checkpoints at every major street, bombing in many areas, sometimes there are battles in their own neighborhood and they cannot get to the office. Many times, my staff has problems outside work—sometimes they have family members who have been kidnapped, sometimes they've been threatened by terrorist groups for working in the government. When they try to do field work there are so many dangers, often they can't get to the measuring sites, or if they get samples they can't get them to the laboratories. We want to cover all Iraq, but we cannot, some areas are just too dangerous."

ACCESSION TO MULTILATERAL TREATIES

The *peshmerga* within Othman kept insisting she fight on, and she managed to keep her ministry focused on the essential issues facing her nation's environment. With a miniscule budget and only a limited opportunity to engage in fieldwork, she concentrated on establishing legal protections for Iraq's environmental assets. Knowing the only way to fully protect Iraq's natural areas was to make it illegal to destroy them, she set about drafting Iraq's first environmental protection laws and its first accessions to legally binding environmental treaties. And against all odds, in the midst of chaos and civil war, she steadfastly forced Parliament to pay attention.

The first major international agreement Othman focused on was the Ramsar Convention on Wetlands, an intergovernmental treaty intended to provide a framework for national action and international cooperation for the conservation of wetlands. Ramsar works like the Olympics—every three years, all the countries that have joined the convention get together and compete for recognition of their conservation efforts. Some of the world's most talented wetlands scientists gather and share technical secrets, while foreign ministry bureaucrats release grandiose resolutions either praising or condemning each other.

The Ninth Ramsar Conference of the Parties (COP) was held in Uganda in November 2005. Clay Rubec helped organize an official Iraqi delegation to attend as observers. Canada, IMELS, and UNEP together funded five delegates from Iraq's Ministries of the Environment and Water Resources. The delegation, headed by Hassan

Janabi, was warmly received at the meeting, which officially noted:

> *Iraq made a statement noting that it was attending COP9 as an observer, but would soon accede to the Convention and participate at COP10 as a Contracting Party. The eastern part of the famous Mesopotamian Marshes would be submitted as the country's first Ramsar site. Iraq wished to recognize the assistance provided by the Canadian International Development Agency (CIDA), UNEP, the U.S. Mission in Baghdad, and the Italian Ministry of Environment. Iraq considered its presence at COP9 to be an indicator of reintegration with the international community after decades of tragic circumstances. Iraq's statement was received by applause.*

Back in Iraq, Othman and Hassan Janabi undertook the political wrangling necessary to achieve ratification of the Ramsar Convention. They doggedly pursued the issue through two of the worst years of violence in Iraq's turbulent history. Sectarian trouble ran rampant through the country; between the summers of 2006 and 2007, over 40,000 people died in terrorist attacks, and by 2008, over four million Iraqis (16% of the population) had become refugees. Othman and Janabi persevered in their task and fnally achieved success: Iraq deposited its accession instrument in October 2007.

Iraq's obligatory first Wetland of International Importance, Hawizeh, covers an enormous 500 square miles (1,300 km²). By designating that one single marsh, Iraq immediately ranked among the top half of countries with respect to the acreage of wetlands protected under Ramsar.

After the Ramsar Convention was signed by the Iraqi Parliament, Othman pushed the United Nations Convention to Combat Desertification through to ratification. But the most significant and broad-reaching treaty that Othman shepherded through the largely-dysfunctional Iraqi Parliament was the UN Convention on Biodiversity (CBD). This convention is based on the philosophy of sustainable use of our planet's finite biological resources. While acknowledging that ecosystems, species and genes must benefit humans, the program argues that these resources should not be used in ways that lead to the long-term decline of biological diversity.

When Othman took over as minister, Iraq was one of only four countries in the world that had not yet signed this treaty. For five years, she worked patiently yet persistently, struggling to move it through the Justice Ministry, the Council of Ministers, and Parliament. On July 28, 2009, Iraq ratified the treaty, leaving only the United States, Somalia, and the Holy See outside the convention.

Realizing that the marshlands represent a unique cultural as well as natural heritage, Othman also worked toward designating the marshlands as a World Heritage Site, a program administered by the United Nations Education, Scientific, and Cultural Organization (UNESCO) that recognizes and protects places that have outstanding cultural or natural importance to the common heritage of humanity. Today, almost 1,000 World Heritage Sites exist, including Greece's Acropolis, Australia's Great Barrier Reef, Peru's Machu Picchu, and the United States' Yellowstone National Park.

Iraq acceded to the treaty in 1974 and successfully listed several archaeological sites but had never nominated a site under the criteria for natural heritage. In 2003, the Mesopotamian Marshlands were placed on Iraq's Tentative List through the joint efforts of the Ministries of Culture and Environment, but UNESCO rejected the application. In 2008, UNESCO entered into a cooperative agreement with Iraq's Ministry of Environment to complete the designation of the marshlands as a World Heritage Site, but as of 2011 the international agency had not yet issued their approval.

In addition to signing existing international treaties, Othman directed her tireless attention to the almost complete lack of environmental laws in Iraq. In 2008, the ministry drafted a law for the establishment of protected areas and nature preserves. For Iraq, the proposed law is highly innovative, including aspects of biodiversity conservation and environmental impact assessment. To enforce these laws, the ministry also proposed the establishment of an environmental police unit.

CONSERVATION AMIDST CHAOS

The ministry's most ambitious project on the ground is the proposed development of the Mesopotamian Marshlands National Park. The idea for the park came at the end of 2005, when a delegation of Iraqis from the Ministry of Municipalities and Public Works traveled to Padua to meet with Italian experts and delineate new projects for the New Eden program. During one of the breaks, Augusto Pretner described a National Park in Sardinia that he had recently assisted the Italian Ministry of Environment (IMELS) to establish. He related how socioeconomic development had been integrated along with the ecological conservation, and one of the participants, Nedaa Jebouri, immediately seized upon the idea of establishing a National Park in the marshlands. A few months later, the proposed project became a joint responsibility between the ministries of Public Works, Environment, and Water Resources.

Iraq has never before designated a National Park, and the Iraqis have relied heavily on Italian expertise to make their dreams a reality. Giorgio Galli agreed to lead the design team with the assistance of key technical leaders Antonia Sopelsa and Mia Fant. Galli, an engineer of remarkable intellectual, moral, and physical stature, has devoted his career to the New Eden project since its inception, and formed strong bonds of friendship with the many Iraqis with whom he has worked. Together the Italians and the Iraqis poured their hearts and minds into creating a plan that is both ecologically and culturally sensitive. The proposed park will incorporate systems to protect the marshes' natural biodiversity, encourage environmental research and education, facilitate ecotourism, allow traditional indigenous activities, and improve the social and economic lives of the local inhabitants.

The planning group first asked the Italians to help select a location for the National Park. Of all the marshes, Hawizeh retains the highest value for biodiversity, but its location near the dangerous Iranian border did not bode well for ecotourism. Furthermore, Hawizeh had already attained legal protection as a designated Ramsar site, and there was a strong desire to codify a similar legal protection to the Central Marshes. The committee eventually selected the Chubayish area of the Central Marshes, a traditional center of the marsh dweller culture that still harbors a rich variety of wetland habitats and wildlife.

The proposed park comprises a core area of protected natural environment surrounded by buffer zones allowing for moderate human usage compatible with conservation objectives. The park itself will cover over 500 square miles (1,300 km^2) spanning three governorates (Dhi Qar, Missan and Basra). It encompasses all of the Chubayish Marsh and the lower portion of the Abu Zirig Marsh, along with areas to the north of these marshes that have not yet been re-flooded.

The proposed Core Zone will be dedicated to the recovery of the marshland ecosystem. Within this space, human activities will be limited to scientific research, environmental monitoring, re-introduction of endangered wildlife, and educational activities. Traditional activities and ecotourism, insofar as they are protective of the environmental qualities of the area, may be allowed but strictly regulated; hunting will be prohibited.

The proposed buffer zone to the north and east of the core area, called The Reserve, will be dedicated to the conservation and re-introduction of wildlife to the marshlands and surrounding areas. The area is currently dry and will probably remain so with some areas seasonally flooded. Within The Reserve, planners envision a Wildlife Conservation Center to be modeled after successful operations in Jordan and Qatar that undertake ex-situ breeding of rare species for re-introduction into their natural environment. The program will focus on marsh-dwelling animals such as the Smooth-coated Otter, the Mesopotamian Gerbil, and the Jungle Cat, and may also include animals such as the Arabian Oryx *(Oryx leucoryx)* and the Mesopotamian Fallow Deer *(Dama dama mesopotamica)* that previously inhabited dry lands around the marshes.

The buffer zone to the west of the Core Area will constitute the proposed "Research Zone," to be used for conservation and environmental research. A Research Center will be built with the primary intent of developing effective capacity among key individuals in the region in wetland management, planning, and monitoring the impacts of natural resources exploitation and their sustainable use. The Research Center will also be used to support educational programs for local and national schools and to house a public interpretive center.

There are currently no permanent human settlements within the Core Zone of the park; the main population centers are located south of the park, between the re-flooded marsh and the Euphrates River. Of particular interest are the refugee marsh dwellers that have re-established their lives in this area. There are now six villages of returned marsh dwellers strung along the Euphrates between the towns of Mdaina and Chubayish. These villages have been rebuilt using traditional reed architecture, and their inhabitants carry on the millennia-old economic activities and marshland-dependent culture practiced by their ancient Sumerian forebears.

The continuation of this traditional lifestyle is essential for the maintenance of many of the park's unique qualities, and the creation of the park is intended to enhance and strengthen the viability of these activities. The southern buffer zone of the Park will be designated the "Traditional Use Zone," where the local inhabitants may actively exercise their rights to fish, graze their water buffalo, and collect reeds for mat weaving.

While the park is still being planned, Nature Iraq has been given the task of creating socioeconomic benefits for the local inhabitants to enable them to see an improvement in their lives associated with environmental conservation. The pilot projects currently being implemented focus on developing a value chain for traditional industries, allowing the local inhabitants to generate additional income from traditional harvesting of natural resources, thereby decrease the need for expanded exploitation of the environment.

The pilot projects include developing a water buffalo demonstration farm to provide local producers with a model of best practices in water buffalo husbandry; the provision of equipment to produce concentrated food for improving the quality of buffalo milk production; further development of the fish cage project; the construction of a fish hatchery to provide fingerlings to increase the production of fish; planting a model date palm orchard to promote new methodologies of date palm cultivation and to provide cuttings to supply new orchards; the refurbishment of existing veterinary centers in Hammar and Chubayish; developing the wildlife center project; and initiating an environmental education program for schoolchildren.

THE GRASSROOTS EFFORT

Saving a nation's environment requires dedicated effort on many levels of organization. While Minister Othman and her staff concentrate on national and international priorities, the ministry's local offices in the governorates struggle diligently to implement their ideas. Nature Iraq's Jassim Asadi, headquartered in Chubayish, is the local driving force behind the development of the Mesopotamian Marshlands National Park. In the marshlands, Jassim can make anything happen. No one knows this ecosystem better, for he was actually born in a *mashuf* deep in the Chubayish marshlands.

"My mother was only seven or eight months pregnant," he recollects, "and she had gone into the marshes that morning to collect reeds. She was working alone and had gone far to find a good spot. I decided to be born there, in a boat in the middle of the marshes, so my first view was reeds and water and my mother."

That was in the 1960s: in those days Chubayish had around 1,600 islands separated by narrow canals, each island holding the houses of one or two families. Everyone went from one island to another in boats. There was one road through the center of town, lined with government offices, schools, and shops, but it wasn't connected to any other roads. The only way to get to Chubayish was by water, so few strangers ever visited.

"We lived in a very small house built of reeds and mud, with my family and three of my father's unmarried brothers," Jassim remembers. "We had a sitting room at one end and a sleeping room at the other. Everyone in the family slept together—the house was built on the earth covered with reed mats that we made ourselves, and we slept right on the mats. We needed very little furniture, because we had very few things to put in cabinets or drawers. In the winter, we would heat the house using the dung of water buffalo for fuel. I never saw electricity until 1974."

"I learned to swim before I could walk and I got my first boat when I was three years old," Jassim continued. "By the time I was six, I would take my *mashuf* into the marshlands every day after school to collect reeds. I always felt happy in the marshes, with the birds and the fish and the people working, always there was someone singing and life felt peaceful."

Jassim was a good student, and his family sent him to live with relatives in the nearby town of Garmat Bani Said so he could attend high school. Afterwards he was accepted to the Mechanical Engineering Department at the University of Baghdad, and a whole new world opened up to him. Like so many others of his generation, he got involved in anti-government politics, arrested by the security police, and tortured, as he says, "in the usual ways." Nevertheless, he eventually was hired by the Ministry of Irrigation. During the 1990s, he realized the ministry was helping to dry the marshlands, but he was powerless against the forces of the Ba'ath government. Unwilling to watch the destruction of his homeland, he moved his family away from the devastation that surrounded Chubayish, but not a day passed that he didn't miss his home.

In June 2003 he was still working for the Ministry of Irrigation when he was assigned to escort Azzam, Hassan Janabi and the USAID team into the marshlands. A partnership was born. In 2004, Jassim conspired with Azzam and Ali Shaheen to re-flood the Chubayish Marshes. Janabi recruited Jassim to work with him in the Center for Restoration of the Iraqi Marshlands, and later Azzam convinced him to join Nature Iraq, where he has accomplished miracles. An enormous source of knowledge about the marshlands and their people, Jassim manages to implement even the most idealistic schemes dreamed up by the Italians, and comes up with his own ingenious ideas as well.

In the old Iraq, the central government made decisions and imposed their will on the local population. In the new Iraq, openness
to local decision-making has emerged. To encourage local stewardship
of the National Park, the planners asked Jassim to convene a committee composed of engineers from the governorate's Ministries of Water
Resources, Environment, and Public Works; professors from nearby
universities; and politicians from the local Governing Councils. With
violence and strife coursing throughout Iraq, the idea of establishing a
broad-reaching, cooperative committee may seem absurd. But traditionally, the tribes of southern Iraq reach decisions not by the dictate
of a sheikh, but through long discussions by a group of tribal elders.
Such groups attempt to reach consensus rather than press forward on
the basis of a majority vote. For three years, the Local Committee has
met on a regular basis to review the proposed pilot projects and to
push toward completion of its goals for the National Park.

The Local Committee is composed of mostly educated people
who live in cement-block houses in the larger towns surrounding the
marshes. In order to fully understand the wishes of the marsh dwellers
themselves, Jassim also formed a Tribal Committee comprising local
leaders who could speak for the wishes of the indigenous people.
He and the Local Committee went from *mudhif* to *mudhif*, giving
PowerPoint presentations to the local tribes, explaining the project
and its ramifications, and listening to their concerns and wishes.

Jassim's life is a whirlwind of activities. Without his efforts, the
National Park would never materialize. Whenever he is asked to
provide anything, his brown face crinkles in thought, and then he
commits to completion, usually by late afternoon. He is the go-to
man for all journalists and dignitaries visiting the marshlands—no
one, it seems, can visit the marshes without him. He convinced the
Italian experts to prepare an Urban Plan for the town of Chubayish,
advocating a series of parks, promenades, schools and clinics for his
hometown. Looking at the trash-strewn waterfront, he organized a
battalion of children who collected the refuse and piled it into the
waiting dump trucks he had arranged. He even dreams of Chubayish
entering the Guinness Book of World Records—for the world's
longest woven reed mat.

As he works to restore his beloved marshlands, his own life has
been dramatically healed. "Now my own family has returned and I am
building my house in Chubayish so that I can see the marshlands again
every day. The town is full of activity—they are constructing three
new schools, a full hospital, and a promenade along the Euphrates

riverfront. Nature Iraq now has an office and a field laboratory here in Chubayish, so we can take samples very easily and analyze them here without going to Basra or Baghdad."

"It is not the simple life anymore. Many things have changed forever. But now every night I go to my Uncle Abu Abbas' *mudhif* and I sit and talk with my friends and family. And every morning I wake up to the sounds of the town coming to life, and I can take my boat and go into the marshlands and know that I helped bring this life back. And sometimes once again … I can hear singing in the marshes."

12. CULTURAL RESURRECTION

In the name of God the Compassionate and the Merciful: "Righteousness does not consist in whether you face towards the east or the west. The righteous man is he who believes in God... who though he loves it dearly, gives away his wealth to kinsfolk, to orphans, to the destitute, to the traveler in need and to beggars..." (2:177) "... Good is the reward of those that do good works in this present life: but far better is the abode of the life to come. Blessed is the abode of the righteous. They shall enter the gardens of Eden, where rivers will roll at their feet; and there shall they have all they desire." (16: 31)

—"The The Holy Quran,
Sura 2, *The Cow*, verse 177and Sura 16, *The Bee*, verse 31

These Iraqi marshlands, a rare watery landscape in the midst of one of the world's largest desert regions, represent a globally significant ecosystem. Its shallow lagoons shelter vast populations of endemic and migratory birds, and its reedy mudflats sustain an abundant and diverse aquatic wildlife. These are not, however, the attributes that have always imbued the marshlands with such romantic idealism. The truly inspiring aspect of these marshlands lies in the unique human culture born and sustained in this ecosystem over the course of millennia.

Determining the number of marsh dwellers—those communities at least partially dependent on the wetland ecosystem for their livelihood and lifestyle—has always proven to be a difficult task. In the 1960s, an estimated 300,000 to 500,000 marsh dwellers lived in and around the marshes. The majority of them were actually agriculturalists tending rice, wheat, and barley fields on the periphery of the marshes; experts at the time estimated that there were only about 50,000 true *ma'dan* living deep within the marshes, subsisting wholly on their bounty through fishing, gaming, buffalo herding, and reed mat weaving. By 1997, the total estimated number of marsh dwellers had fallen to 190,000, with no one actually living within the marshes because they had dried up. By the summer of 2003, aid agencies entering southern Iraq estimated that only 87,000 marsh dwellers remained in the vicinity of the marshes, most of them living in the larger surviving villages such as Chubayish and Mdaina.

The drying of the marshlands and the dispersal of its people to refugee camps and urban slums led most experts to predict the destruction of its human culture. They reckoned that the vital skills necessary for survival—fishing, gaming, animal husbandry, and mat weaving—would have gradually eroded away during the years of exile. The experts also predicted that few refugees would return to the marshes, even if they were restored. A large percentage of the refugees' adult male population had either been killed or imprisoned during the 1990s, and in this unforgiving environment, groups of women, children, and elderly men could not be expected to provide for themselves. Moreover, the experts concluded, once these destitute people had seen the conveniences offered by the modern world—medical care, education, electricity and television—they would never wish to return to those "swamps."

But return they did. Like the fish streaming back from the rivers, the human exiles gradually migrated home. Family by family, meager possessions in hand, they journeyed southward through Iraq, reuniting with others of their clan, once again immersing themselves into their traditional patterns of life. Back in the marshes again, they harvested the reeds bursting forth from the newly re-flooded land, using them to construct new homes and *mudhif* according to architectural patterns dating back to the early Sumerians. Thousands of *mashuf* appeared seemingly from nowhere, and fishermen eagerly plied the waters streaming over the dried earth. The marsh dwellers readily traded their cattle for water buffalo. No skills had been lost.

The number of people that have returned to the marshes since 2003 has not been calculated, but estimates range from 50,000 to 100,000. Improved environmental conditions and their subsequent boost to the economy have swelled the populations of the nearby towns. However, the marsh dwellers returned to a complete dearth of services and economic opportunities beyond those offered by the resurging natural environment. During the 1970s and 1980s, basic medical care and a rudimentary primary education had been provided within the larger villages along the periphery of the marshlands, and the *ma'dan* dwelling deep within the reeds had at least limited access to those services. Now, the rebuilt villages had nothing—not even a supply of safe drinking water. Health care and educational services in the larger towns such as Chubayish and Mdaina had likewise suffered during the persecution by Saddam's regime and were wholly inadequate to the challenge of providing for the rapidly burgeoning populations of the returning emigrants.

Thus these people who had suffered so much under Saddam continued to suffer after his removal. The newly-developing democracy in Iraq did, however, yield at least one new dimension to their lives: the freedom of association. They found that groups spoke louder than individuals and that by working together they could garner more attention to their needs and achieve a better resolution of their grievances. A civil society mentality was born.

WHAT DO THE MARSH DWELLERS WANT?

The Marsh Arab Forum, held in December 2004, was the first conference to be convened within the marshlands of Iraq. Organized by local activists, its purpose was to bring together the disparate stakeholders—local tribal leaders, government officials, and scientific experts—to focus on the restoration of the marshlands and the provision of services to its people. Such a gathering may seem commonplace to westerners, but nothing of its kind had ever taken place in Iraq. Bringing together tribal leaders from three different governorates presented enormous diplomatic hurdles. Each leader travelled with a retinue of advisors and armed guards, each tribe had experienced problems with every other tribe in the past, and the protocol and etiquette for seating and introductions took weeks to organize. The idea of including scientific experts was revolutionary; university professors simply did not meet with tribal leaders. Government officials were accustomed to meeting with tribal leaders, but only when the locals went to their offices, not the other way around.

A delegation was sent to Baghdad to ask Nature Iraq to help plan, organize, and fund the project. Azzam agreed to match the money donated by the local people, and he helped them develop the list of participants and an agenda. They selected the small town of Islah, at the head of the recently re-flooded Abu Zirig marsh, as the locale. The local Ministry of Municipalities and Public Works provided office space to help organize the conference.

On a crisp December morning the participants arrived, walking from the local villages, driving by car from as far away as Amara, Basra, and Baghdad, even poling a small flotilla of *mashuf* from the interior of the re-flooded marsh. Word had spread, and although only 200 official invitations had been issued, over 400 people showed up. A local artist, Kamil Moussawi, had set up an exhibition of his work, and participants mingled amongst his brightly colored renderings of marshland scenes while the politics of seating arrangements were hastily reworked.

The meeting began with a reading of the Koran, followed by a speech from the governor of Dhi Qar and various other ministry officials. After the opening remarks, the conference participants boarded motor boats and puttered into the northern portion of Abu Zirig marsh along the main canals. Thick reed beds, in some places over ten feet (3 m) tall, had grown over the last year. The boats threaded their way through the reed forest, dodging fishermen's nets strung throughout the lagoons. As the locals discussed their own fishing economy, the scientists marveled at the extent of the restoration, and the government officials began to fully realize why these people so deeply desired the return of more marshlands.

The participants disembarked at the *mudhif* of the local sheikh, who had slaughtered 55 sheep to feed the crowd a delicious lunch prepared by the local women of the village. Afterward, a smaller meeting was organized for the presentation of scientific papers at the Governor's office in Nasriya, which lasted well into the night and was only interrupted due to the loss of electrical power. The meeting continued the next day at the Genoob Hotel, with well over 100 participants.

The group agreed on the importance of restoring the marshes to their natural state while at the same time developing the human potential of the returning marsh dwellers. They cited the need to develop infrastructure and services in a manner protective of the fragile wetland environment. Safe drinking water was the primary demand of the local people, but the participants also argued for increased interaction with the outside world, including the development of roads and transportation systems and the provision of electricity and communications. Many at the meeting expressed concern over the deplorable state of health care in the marshland area; they demanded the development of clinics and hospitals in the larger villages and discussed the possibility of a floating health care system that could circulate amongst the smaller settlements. Education was a common theme, stressing opportunities for women, remedial education for elders, and compulsory elementary school for all children. They also called for the prohibition of fishing methods that stress the environment, such as the use of poisons, pesticides, explosives, and electric fishing.

MODERN DEVELOPMENT IN THE MARSHLANDS

Azzam attended the meeting and listened carefully to the demands of the people. The call for increased restoration and protection of the marshes impressed him, although the demands for increased roads and infrastructure in the marshlands gave him cause for concern. Properly designed, these accoutrements of modern life could benefit the local population while preserving the natural environment. Improperly designed, elevated earthen roadways could transform the free-flowing marshlands into a series of stagnant ponds. Schools and clinics—vital for the development of the human element in the marshlands—could be situated on elevated building pads well out of the reach of floods, or they could be built at ground level, necessitating the construction of dykes around villages to protect the new infrastructure while ruining the traditional water-based design of the village itself.

Azzam firmly believed that the marsh dwellers deserve all the necessities and conveniences of modern life, and he had an equally deep conviction that those elements of contemporary life could be introduced without endangering the sensitive wetlands environment or destroying the traditional way of life. He had just returned from a conference at Harvard University, "The Mesopotamian Marshlands and Modern Development," where Dr. Robert France had led a panel of experts who ended with the same conclusion. There were no inherent conflicts between the modern world and the marshlands, if—and that was a big if—the design carefully considered the preservation of the natural environment along with the traditional lifestyle it had engendered.

Azzam approached the Italian experts of the New Eden Team with this new problem. Experienced with international development aid programs, they told him that the first step toward strategizing for development would be to define the existing situation of the infrastructure and quantify the actual needs and desires of the local population. Funded by the Italian Ministry of the Environment, Giorgio Galli (we call him the human work machine) agreed to undertake the task of conducting an extensive socioeconomic survey covering three governorates of the marshlands.

The survey found that clean drinking water was the number one priority of the marsh dwellers—and for good reason. The team enumerated only 300 water treatment plants serving a total population of 5 million. Only the major towns and cities had a municipal water supply system. Although this meant that 80% of the population at least theoretically had a secure source of drinking water—albeit of low quality—the majority of the human settlements lacked any public water supply system. The people in these smaller settlements either drank directly from the rivers and marshes or used virtually all of their meager earnings to buy water trucked in by commercial suppliers.

The situation for the treatment of wastewater was far worse, with only about a tenth of the settlements having a sewage system, servicing less than a quarter of the total population (nationally, three-quarters of the population has sewage facilities). None of the systems were located within the marshlands. The lack of wastewater facilities poses serious challenges to the maintenance of health in these villages, leading to increased waterborne diseases such as typhoid and cholera.

In the larger marshland towns such as Chubayish and Hammar City, toilet waste typically goes directly into underground cesspools or covered pits adjacent to the houses; wastewater from sinks and showers is drained to open ponds between homes. The conditions in marshland villages are worse. People bathe and wash directly in the rivers and marshes and defecate in outdoor toilets adjacent to their homes, typically directly over the water used for other household purposes, sometimes even for drinking.

With respect to availability of health care, the New Eden survey found only 32 hospitals and 199 medical centers servicing 5 million people. One standard measurement of the adequacy of hospital facilities is the ratio of the human population to the available hospital beds. In the U.S., for example, there are 32 hospital beds per 10,000 people; in these three provinces, there are 11 hospital beds per 10,000 people. Even the ratios in nearby countries are much better, including Jordan at 18, Egypt at 17, and Lebanon at 35.

No medical services at all are provided in the marshes themselves. Anyone following a traditional lifestyle in the re-flooded marshes must travel by boat just to reach a road; from there, they must somehow obtain ground transport to the nearest large town to find a rudimentary clinic. Hospitals are found only in the larger towns and for the most part remain very poorly staffed and equipped. In reality, when a marsh dweller gets sick they generally remain at home and pray for recovery.

The educational system has improved somewhat more rapidly than the health care system. The New Eden survey enumerated 2,500 primary, intermediate, and secondary schools enrolling almost a million children, approximately half of the school-age population. Most of the smaller villages usually have only a primary school; children whose families can afford to have them attend secondary school take up residence with city relatives or in dormitories run by the schools or by entrepreneurs. Some of the marshland girls never attend school at all, and the majority of the boys quit after learning reading and arithmetic in the third grade.

Iraq has a rich educational tradition dating back to the establishment of Baghdad's Mustansiriya Madrasa in 1227, one of the first universities in the world. Nevertheless it is surprising that such a poor area has so many higher educational facilities; the New Eden survey found 46 colleges and universities in the three governorates. All of these, however, suffered from poor facilities and generally under-trained teaching staff.

The surveyors also took the opportunity to quantitatively evaluate people's attitudes toward the marshes and their restoration. Those surveyed overwhelmingly agreed that marsh dwellers have a right to return to their original villages, and they also expressed an unexpectedly high respect for wildlife and the environment, strongly agreeing that animals and plants have the right to exist even they though may be of no use to mankind. They maintained a clear vision of a sustainable economy and environment, expressing the belief that it was right to sacrifice their current income and standard of living so that the next generation should benefit from preservation of the earth's natural environment.

POSTWAR RECONSTRUCTION

Numerous international aid agencies, along with the new Iraqi government, have worked toward rectifying the dearth of services in southern Iraq. Due to the difficult security situation during recent years, the humanitarian aid agencies that have continued to operate have done so under strict secrecy. As a result, reports and statistics of the aid that has actually been implemented on the ground have not been compiled, and it is beyond the capability of this book to enumerate all the projects that have benefited the people of the area. Yet those efforts still fall short of the needs.

Humanitarian agencies including USAID, AMAR Appeal, the Salvation Army, Mercy Corps, and People in Need have all contributed greatly to the provision of essential services to the people of southern Iraq. The Iraqi government itself has been the largest benefactor, building numerous new schools and rehabilitating and staffing health care clinics and hospitals in the larger towns and villages. Small primary schools have even been built in the villages of the returning marsh dwellers.

But developing permanent health clinics in the marshlands themselves—along with the difficulty of attracting and keeping city-trained nurses and doctors within the extremely challenging and remote environment—remains problematic, given the difficulty of maintaining adequate facilities in an area that is periodically flooded and dried. For most of the marshes the best plan would be to develop floating mobile clinics to circulate throughout the marshland areas, treating diseases, vaccinating children, and educating the people about basic sanitation and health procedures. Some clinics near the marshes have begun to informally carry out such periodic visits, but in order to fully address the health needs of the marsh dwellers a stronger commitment and capital investment in the plan is required.

The UNEP postwar project played a leading role in the provision of clean drinking water to the villages of returning marsh dwellers. In 2006, UNEP contracted with Nature Iraq to design and install Reverse Osmosis (RO) drinking water treatment plants in six villages, bringing safe drinking water for more than 20,000 people. In 2007, IMELS contracted with Nature Iraq to design and install an additional three RO units to provide water for an additional 3,000 people in smaller marshland villages. UNEP also contracted with Nature Iraq to supervise construction of a demonstration wastewater treatment system in Chubayish. This system used constructed wetlands to treat the domestic wastewater and serves approximately 200 people.

NEW EDEN VILLAGES

Azzam watched the gradual improvement in human services in the marshland areas with some satisfaction, yet he yearned to go beyond this piecemeal provision of services. He envisioned entire villages provided with all relevant services integrated within their traditional patterns of life. Azzam wanted the marsh dwellers to have modern services and conveniences provided in an environmentally sensitive manner. He envisioned traditional reed villages with electricity provided through solar cells, communication through wireless technology, clean drinking water through small RO units, and sewage treatment via portable compact units.

Azzam took these ideas to the Italian experts and related his vision to Marco Oliviero, who enthusiastically embraced the concept and quickly became one of the project's strongest proponents. After extended study of the traditional culture of the marshlands, the project of a single village grew into a vision of several prototype villages. The first type, called the water village, would represent the traditional marshland settlements; these would be based on groupings of around 50 individual islands, with the layout designed according to historical satellite images of real villages. Basic services provided in the water villages would include electricity, clean drinking water, and sustainable economic opportunities.

Oliviero also developed the concept of waterfront villages— larger developments historically found lining the major canals that provided ingress and egress to the marshlands. Such villages were traditionally more developed than the isolated villages deep in the marshlands, and the design team envisioned expanded services here, including a primary school, clinic, veterinary center, wireless internet access, markets, and mosque, all of which would be available to provide outreach care and services to the water villages deeper within the marshlands.

In the Iraqi government, the primary champion of the New Eden Villages was Nedaa Jebouri from the Ministry of Municipalities and Public Works. The idea would never have blossomed without her stewardship and sharp intellect. Most of the men she worked with lived in terror of her occasionally incisive remarks, but to western women she was a symbol of the potential strength of the Iraqi female. Before she could realize the dream of the New Eden villages, however, Nedaa's life came to a tragic end. On the morning of February 27, 2007, Vice President Adel Abdul Mahdi entered the auditorium at the headquarters of the Ministry of Municipalities and Public Works to publicly commend the outstanding achievements of its staff in the reconstruction of their country. Nedaa sat in the front row, eager as always to hear and question. The bomb hidden under those seats very likely killed her instantly.

Bereft of their champion, the New Eden Villages remain only in blueprints.

JOBS AND INCOME

Beyond increasing access to social services to the marsh dwellers, their economic opportunities must be increased to provide for a secure future. Many outsiders have suggested that the dried marshes could be converted to field agriculture to provide more income for the local people, but the soils of the marshlands have too much salt and too little drainage to support the production of barley or wheat, the staple crops of central Iraq. The economy of the marshlands must necessarily be based upon exploitation of its natural resources—reeds, fish, and birds. But increased harvesting of those resources could significantly deteriorate its fragile ecological balance. Therefore, it is important to find a means of increasing the value chain of the products taken from the marshes, to reduce their overall exploitation while maximizing the economic gain to the local inhabitants. In addition to the fisheries and aquaculture projects already discussed, the most substantive economic opportunities for the marsh dwellers remain those that have traditionally dominated in this area—dairy production, date palm orchards, and reed mat weaving.

WATER BUFFALO HUSBANDRY

No marsh dweller family is complete without several water buffalo, and those specializing in buffalo breeding may have a hundred or more of the lumbering beasts. Their dairy products are prized throughout Iraq. Water buffalo milk, creamy and thick, has twice the fat content and substantially more protein and calcium than cow's milk, while containing much less cholesterol. The milk may be drank fresh, but it is more usually made into yogurt, cheese, and a type of smoky cream cheese known as *ghaymer*.

Before 1990, an estimated 200,000 water buffalos wallowed in these wetlands. During the 1990s, as the marsh dwellers emigrated from the drying marshes, they either brought these valuable livestock along on their exile, foraging for reeds along the riverbanks, or sold their animals at a loss. When the marsh dwellers returned, they began to exchange the dry-land cattle for their beloved water buffalo, and buffalo populations rapidly soared.

Nadheer Abood began his work with Nature Iraq as its point man for water buffalo issues. He recognizes the tremendous economic impact of this species for the marsh dwellers and has been charmed by the close relationship between the buffalo herders and their charges. "The human, the marsh and the buffalo are just like a triangle," he says. "If you remove any line of it the other lines would collapse."

The New Eden study determined that the most useful ways to increase the dairy industry's value to the local people include reducing the loss of livestock by improving the level of veterinary care available to the buffalo herders; increasing milk production through improved feedstock; and developing milk collection and processing centers in the larger villages to provide additional jobs for the local people. Pilot projects are being implemented in the Chubayish and Abu Zirig marsh areas as part of the Mesopotamian Marshlands National Park program.

DATE PALM INDUSTRY

The tall swaying fronds of the date palm, called *nakhla* in Iraq, have formed a constant backdrop for Iraq's cultural and economic heritage since Sumerian times. Myths and ritual surround the revered tree; it is even said that palm trees can fall in love, as some female palms will accept pollination from only a single lifetime mate. Nearly every established household boasts several trees producing dates for their own domestic use; the average Iraqi consumes around 15 pounds (7 kg) of this sweet fruit each year. Sometimes they are eaten out of hand, either fresh or dried, or drizzled with sesame paste and immersed in creamy fresh buffalo yogurt. Sometimes they are stuffed with walnuts, and on special occasions they are chopped for filling pastries. Bread dipped in date syrup, or *dibbis*, is a breakfast staple throughout Iraq.

Historically, vast forests of date palms lined the banks of the southern Euphrates and the Shatt al-Arab Rivers, irrigated twice a day as the rising tide from the Gulf pushed water levels up into the network of canals that crisscrossed the groves. For many decades, Iraq produced the world's gold standard of dates, commanding three-quarters of the global market. But the Iran-Iraq war decimated the great palm groves of the Shatt al-Arab; perhaps half of Iraq's palm trees—formerly estimated at 20 to 40 million—were destroyed during the hostilities. During his attack on the marshes, Saddam Hussein ordered all palm trees within the drained marshes decapitated. After the construction of large dams on the Euphrates, the flow of freshwater through the Shatt al-Arab decreased, and saltwater intruded upstream. The subsequent increased salinity further damaged any remaining riverbank groves. Even more loss occurred in the aftermath of the 2003 war and its subsequent civil unrest, as pesticides became unavailable and disease took its toll on the valuable trees. Iraq's Ministry of Agriculture estimates that only 10 million trees are left in Iraq, with scarcely three to four million within its southern provinces where they once grew most densely.

A thriving date palm industry could create tens of thousands of jobs for Iraqis. It is a labor-intensive crop that requires hand pruning, pollination, harvesting and marketing of the dates. Before the Iran-Iraq war, hundreds of thousands of families were employed in date production. Iraq's output has fallen to a third of its former level, and the lack of security frustrates efforts to export product. A revived date culture could represent a billion-dollar industry for the country.

USAID's postwar marshland program immediately recognized the value of Iraq's date industry, and in 2004 they established eight date palm nurseries containing a total of 4,500 trees of 21 varieties in the vicinity of the marshlands. Within a few years of planting, each palm produces offshoots that are then cut and planted in new orchards; these new palms will be distributed among additional marsh dwellers.

With funding from IMELS, Nature Iraq is currently undertaking the construction of two more date palm orchards near the Mesopotamian Marshlands National Park, hoping that the re-introduction of the lucrative date production will decrease utilization of other natural resources in and around the National Park. The area near Abu Zirig marsh was selected as the location because it has good soil, open areas, and most importantly, a regular supply of fresh, low-salinity water from the Gharraf River. The orchard is designed as a center for demonstration of the best practices in Integrated Pest Management, fertilization, and drip irrigation.

HANDICRAFTS

The weaving of reed mats is a mainstay of the marshland economy. Entire families participate in the manufacturing process, utilizing techniques that have changed little from Sumerian times. Every day, trucks arrive from Basra to be loaded up with the woven mats, which are used extensively throughout Iraq and the Gulf, and of course require annual replacement.

Basket weaving, however, is practiced almost exclusively by women. The finest baskets are woven from palm fronds instead of reeds. At the present time, women weave only for the use of their own household; no outlets for commercial sale have been developed. The most typical basket uses a coiled technique. Slender reeds form the foundation of the basket, and the women wrap split palm fronds around the foundation to form the finished product. Toys, including small *mudhif* models, are also sometimes crafted to entertain the children.

Saadia al-Salhy, founder of Together to Protect Women and the Environment, and Intisar Alramahi of the Ibn Sina Society, have led Nature Iraq's efforts to find ways to improve the status of women in the marshlands by providing them with increased economic opportunities. They have concluded that basket production may serve as one such possibility, but the techniques and skills of the local women deteriorated significantly during the 1990s' forced emigration from the marshlands. Nature Iraq plans to initiate competitions in the marshlands to encourage development, sharing and improvement of traditional basket weaving techniques.

MARSHLANDS CULTURAL MUSEUM

The display of handicraft production is planned as a key feature of the Marshlands Cultural Museum currently under construction near Chubayish. The proposal for the center was a collaborative effort between Hassan Janabi in the Ministry of Water Resources and Maysoon Damluji, Iraq's Deputy Minister of Culture from 2004 through 2006.

Three distinct yet interconnected museums have been proposed. The Natural History Exhibit, where live species of fish and plants can be observed in motion and studied, will include an aquarium displaying examples of river and marsh water life. The Archeology Museum will focus on the cultures that inhabited the region throughout history. The Popular Heritage Museum will introduce the arts and crafts of the local people to visitors, allowing them to observe craftsmen and women at work and to purchase local handicrafts. A laboratory and specialized library will serve resident and visiting researchers.

Within half a decade, the Iraqi government had moved from attempting to exterminate the marshland culture to celebrating and preserving their indigenous traditions.

13. DROUGHT AND DESPAIR

"May An not change the divine plans for treating the people with justice ... that the Tigris and Euphrates should again carry water ... that there should be rain in the skies and ... water courses with water ... that the marshes should support fish and fowl ... that old reeds and fresh reeds should grow in the reed beds.."

—Lamentation for Sumer (circa 2000 BC)

Ragged dark clouds scuttled across the sky as I contemplated the vast history of this land. It was January 2009 and we had been driving on a raised dirt embankment through a still-dry portion of Hammar Marsh when suddenly we spied a small hill, no more than a quarter mile (0.4 km) in diameter but rising abruptly about 50 feet (15 m) above the broad flat plain that stretched for hundreds of miles around us. The hill floated above the sea of desert shrubs like a ghostly galleon adrift in a sudden squall. As lightning flashed around us, the knoll seemed to list and keel in the biting wind.

"We call it Tell Sho'aib," our local guide explained. "Do you want to see it?"

A few minutes later we stood on the crest of the hill looking down at the dark soil littered with potsherds: millions of fragments of pottery covered the entire mound. I plucked one from the ground; dusting it off, I found my fingers tracing an ancient indentation. A pattern had been roughly etched into the wet mud with a crude implement, probably a reed, and the design immediately reminded me of the Sumerian pottery I had recently been studying. The simple, unglazed fragment lay heavy in my hand, weighty with the memory of millennia.

Tell Sho'aib probably dates to pre-Sumerian times, although it has yet to be excavated by archaeologists. Our guide pointed toward the eastern horizon; in the distance, another knoll rose sharply above the plain, part of a string of mounds leading back toward Eridu and Ur. These were the settlements of the Sumerians—islands of villages anchored in the lush lagoons of their ancient gods. Thousands of years ago, surrounded by wetlands, these knolls sheltered the cultures of the Sumerians, the Sealanders, and the Chaldeans. And for thousands of years they have stood sentinel over the land, watching as wave after wave of immigrants and invaders crashed over their domain. The tells stood firm as Assyrians, Mongols, Persians and Arabs clashed for control of this ungovernable wilderness. They stood and continue to stand at the nexus of our common heritage.

Palpable reminders of the most recent struggle for control were spread before us like a carpet of contempt. Once the mound had risen proudly above a sea of emerald-green reeds; now it squatted amidst a tumble of scorched desert scrub. Saddam's assault on the marshlands had dealt the final blow: where Sargon and Sennacherib had failed, he had succeeded in obliterating one of the largest wetland ecosystems of the world.

Our truck lurched eastward on the raised roadway toward the former Hammar Lake, where we suddenly passed out of the desert scrub and into a moonscape of barren soil. Just a few decades earlier, Hammar Lake had covered hundreds of square miles with sparkling water, filled with a rich abundance of fish and fish-eating wildlife. Now we drove for miles over the dry lake bed.

We stopped and clambered down the embankment to get a closer look. From this vantage, my geologist's eyes clearly discerned an artificial surface: apparently hundreds of square miles had been bulldozed after the lake had been drained. Bits of dried twigs and reed scattered the surface, lying amidst whitewashed shells of snail and mollusk. Azzam and I walked northward as far as we could, the wet mud clinging heavily to our feet, but could not find a natural surface. An army of earth-moving equipment had wiped the slate clean.

Everywhere we went on that trip, we found grisly reminders of Saddam's brutal assault. Jassim Asadi took us to examine the ruined settlements of the Central Marshes, the villages beloved by Thesiger, Maxwell and Young. All of them had been destroyed. At Ishan Qubba we walked through the deserted islands of a marsh town that once sheltered thousands of people but now stood completely bereft of humanity. Without water or vegetation, the ashen islands stood out like raised welts against the rich organic mud of the former reed beds. I conjured up the thriving community, its waterways teeming with *mashuf*, its islands lively with reed huts. I ran my hands through the grey dust, fingering the ashes of those burnt reeds, the detritus of those charred homes and destroyed lives. I could almost hear the helicopter gunships circling as I envisioned soldiers with AK-47s invading the *mudhif*, frightening people and herding them onto pontoon boats. I could smell their lives burning.

But we also saw hope for the future. The National Park project has an advisory committee composed of tribal leaders, and Jassim arranged a meeting with the Abu Zirig group headed by Sheikh Sayyid Jameel al-Yeshua. *Thesiger would be rolling in his grave*, I thought, as I doffed my muddy boots and stepped onto the rich carpet of the al-Yeshua *mudhif*, usually a males-only domain. This was my first experience in a sheikh's guesthouse and I stood soaking in its smoky ambience as sunlight flickered through the open weave of its reed walls. With a flourish of his cape and a genuinely warm smile, Sayyid Jameel invited Azzam to sit next to him at the head of the *mudhif* and gestured for me to sit on his other side. We sipped thick coffee while the men animatedly discussed the National Park project, interrupted by the occasional cell phone call as the sheikhs dealt with the next day's local elections. I found the blending of tradition and modernity somewhat disconcerting, but the men obviously saw no contradiction between the highly ritualized social interactions within the *mudhif* and the casual wireless telecommunication with the outside world.

Travelling westward, we once again boarded a few *balam* and chugged down a canal into the northwestern corner of the Hammar Marshes. Winding through the vegetation-choked waterway we reached an open expanse of water and spied a sight of pure joy: a true water-village. The al-Winais clan, returning to their ancestral homeland, had found their original man-made islands intact, and when Shaheen opened the regulators on the Euphrates the surrounding land flooded, reeds sprouted, fish wriggled in, and their way of life regained their traditional patterns.

"WE ARE DYING FOR WATER"

The next day, Nature Iraq's KBA team arrived in Chubayish, continuing their twice-yearly survey of southern Iraq, and the office and dormitory surged with their exuberance. Mudhafar showed me amazing photographs of their work so far—thousands of pink flamingoes temporarily sheltering in a saline wetland near Sanaf, over a hundred thousand migratory waders in Dalmaj Lake, a million water birds in southern Hawizeh. He excitedly related their discovery of two spring-fed oases in the southwestern foothills of the Zagros Mountains, one with unusually sulfurous waters, a unique ecosystem to explore in the future.

With the birders by our side, we journeyed back into the marshes, appreciating them in a whole new way. Chugging up the wide channel from Abu Subatt, Mudhafar pointed out a Pied Kingfisher (Ceryle rudis) hovering over the water, its black-and-white body twisted into a tight horseshoe as he peered down and then suddenly jackknifed into the water. Its more flamboyant cousin, known by the somewhat inadequate moniker of White-breasted Kingfisher (Halcyon smyrnensis), flashed his iridescent blue back as it skimmed over the reeds. Little Grebes (Tachybaptus ruficollis), disturbed by our boat, flapped over the water then dove in; lacking proper tail feathers, they prefer swimming rather than flying. Purple Gallinules or Swamphen (Porphyrio porphyrio) giggled behind the reed curtain, competing with the chirruping of the tiny Chiffchaff (Phylloscopus collybita).

As we neared Birkat Baghdadiya, Mudhafar silenced the motors, and the boatmen slowly poled us along. I gave myself over to the mood of the marshes, listening to the soft scrape of the boat against the reeds, catching a tantalizing glimpse of a large Grey Heron (Ardea cinerea) perched like a statue behind the reeds. We floated past small ponds hidden within the forest of reeds, their waters covered with yellow blossoms like a spring meadow. The boatmen anxiously pointed to rooted-up reeds: wild boar have returned to the marshes in good numbers and once again threaten the unwary marsh visitor.

At the lake Mudhafar donned his wading pants, hung his camera with its foot-long telephoto lens around his neck, and sloshed out to count the teeming birds barely visible in the distance. As I watched, hundreds of Marbled Ducks (Marmaronetta angustirostris) flew in and settled down with their cousins. Then a huge flock of Black-tailed Godwit (Limosa limosa) burst up, zigzagged left and right and then settled back down to feed. A circling Western Marsh Harrier (Circus aeruginosus) ignored them. The guide explains to me that the harrier prefers the Common Coot (Fulica atra), locally known as "water chicken," because they are dim-witted and easy to catch. Mudhafar waded back through a flock of Black-winged Stilts (Himantopus himantopus), their orange legs high-stepping through the mud. He has counted thousands of birds in this small lake alone.

But the water level in Baghdadiya was too shallow for our boats to enter. Traveling past the lake, the boatmen had to pole our *balam* through channels where last year we had sped through deep water. Finally the channel dried entirely and we continued northward on foot. Eventually we found an encampment of marsh dwellers on the northern edge of Chubayish Marsh—the Ghadban clan, living in a dozen reed huts hastily constructed on the dry ground near the destroyed village of Hallab. Hundreds of water buffalo lolled about, sleeping heavily in the afternoon sun, while children played happily at the edge of the water. They told us they usually lived with relatives in the nearby town of Majar al-Kabir, but that week was a school holiday so they were visiting their marshland homes. The men gathered around Azzam, eager to talk to him. They complained that after the re-flooding they had never been able to drink the water here, but now the high salinity of the water was adversely affecting the health of their buffalo. Their milk production had fallen to a fraction of the usual volume, and now disease was taking an increasing toll on their valuable livestock.

"We are dying for water," they told him. "You must tell Baghdad to help us."

We returned south in the boats and entered the Euphrates River, alarmed to discover that its level stood several feet (1 m) lower than it had than the year before. Jassim informed us that the flow of water in the Euphrates at Nasriya had fallen to less than 20% of its volume two years before.

We motored across the diminished Euphrates towards its southern bank. Water no longer flowed from the Euphrates into the Hammar Marsh; the boatmen had to disembark and push us over the rim of the breached levee into the shallow water of the remaining wetland. The first portion of the marsh sparkled with fresh green reeds and lively birds, but as we puttered further away from the Euphrates, the water level decreased ominously. Muddy salt crusts covered the base of the reeds extending six inches (15 cm) up from the water line. Outside the channel, salt crystals sparkled in the damp ground.

Deep in the marsh we found an encampment of marsh dwellers, the Baher clan, struggling to survive as the water slowly disappeared. The men told us that after Saddam dried the Hammar Marsh in the 1990s, they had migrated with their water buffalo northward along the Euphrates to Bellad, where there were some limited marshes to sustain their herds; they had returned here a few years ago when the marshes were restored. But now their buffalo were dying and they faced another migration out of the home they loved.

As we left, I bent down to kiss one of the women farewell and she firmly grasped my shoulders, gazing intently at my face. We were roughly the same age, but I could see decades of tragedy in her eyes. "If these marshes die, I might as well die with them," she told me. "I have lived through this before and I cannot live through it again."

CAMPAIGN FOR THE 7/12 DAM

Back at the Nature Iraq office, Jassim proposed an unlikely measure to temporarily restore water to the marshes of the Euphrates. When Saddam built the Glory Canal through the Central Marshes, it released such a large amount of water at its terminus into the Euphrates that a dam had to be constructed between Mdaina and Chubayish to keep the water from flowing upstream. After the fall of Saddam, this dam had been partially destroyed. If it were rebuilt, it would raise the water levels in the Euphrates west of the dam and cause water to flow back into the Chubayish marsh. The structure, known as the 7/12 dam, would not halt the flow of water through to the Shatt al-Arab, only temporarily store it in the marshes.

The plan was brilliantly simple. Azzam called Andrea Cattarossi and described the proposed action to him, and Andrea immediately tasked his Italian engineers with designing the new dam.

The next day we flew to Baghdad and began to campaign for the project. Azzam was like a man on fire, making a dozen phone calls before breakfast to set up meetings to cover the one day we had available in the capital. Our first destination was a known ally— the Center for Restoration of the Iraqi Marshlands. Abdul Kadum Lahmoud, the General Director of CRIM, was aware of the problem; his staff closely monitored the health of the marshes via interpretation of satellite images, the IMOS project inherited from UNEP's Hassan Partow. Just that day they had determined that the percentage of re-flooded marshlands had been drastically reduced over the last few months. In 2006, the re-flooded marshes had covered 71% of their extent in the 1970s. Now the marshes covered only 43% of their former territory.

CRIM had just broken ground on the multi-million dollar project to implement the recommendations of the Master Plan for the marshlands. In two years, these structures would regulate and redirect the flow of water to provide relief to the suffering wetlands. But the marsh dwellers needed water immediately. Azzam described the idea for utilizing the 7/12 dam to Lahmoud. He supported the plan, but could not promise its implementation. Most of the CRIM's resources were devoted to the current construction program; only the MoWR would have the funding to undertake reconstruction of the dam.

So we went to see Dr. Aoun Thiab Abdullah, a senior director at the Ministry of Water Resources and an old friend of Azzam's father, and they reminisced about Jawad while we drank small cups of *numi basra*, dried lime tea. He liked the idea for the 7/12 dam but warned us that the Basra governorate, lying downstream of the dam, might oppose the idea, fearing that it could affect their water quality and supply. Nevertheless, he promised to establish a committee to evaluate the proposal.

The lack of water was no news to the ministry. A year before, they had issued a drought warning and began rationing water for Iraq's thirsty crops. Rain during the 2007/08 water year[11] had been a third of the normal amount, and the drought had continued through the 2008/2009 period. The total rainfall in some areas was only a quarter of the normal amount, amounting to only about four to eight inches (10-20 cm) of precipitation. Wheat and barley production had fallen by half. Conditions were dire across the country: of course the marsh dwellers were suffering like everyone else.

Later that evening, Azzam discussed the 7/12 dam project with Narmin Othman, Iraq's Minister of the Environment, and she agreed to support the project, although her ministry also lacked the resources to implement construction. Then Azzam met with the final key player—the new Chairman of Iraq's Ramsar Committee on Wetlands, Ekram Qassim. Qassim worked in the Prime Minister's office, and Azzam wanted Prime Minister Maliki to be personally apprised of the situation in the marshes. The Maliki tribe belongs to the Muntafiq, a centuries-old confederation of Marsh Arab tribes. The marshes that would be rescued by the 7/12 dam were deep in the Muntafiq homeland.

Then we waited. Months went by with no action. The Nature Iraq

---

[11] Most water resources agencies gauge time by the "water year" which begins on October 1 and ends on September 30.

team decided to initiate a media campaign to highlight the plight of the marsh dwellers and apply political pressure to implement a solution. Jassim Asadi burst into public relations mode. He met with western journalists from Reuters, BBC, National Public Radio, and Fox News; convinced the regional al-Arabiya television station to broadcast a report; and managed to get coverage in all of the major Iraqi television and radio stations. He visited the local government officials in Dhi Qar and presented his idea for the 7/12 dam project, and they adopted the idea enthusiastically. Both the Governor and the Governing Council of Dhi Qar issued official letters to the MoWR and to Prime Minister Maliki's office requesting its immediate implementation.

In March 2009, a MOWR committee approved the design of a temporary structure for the 7/12 dam project. Yet still nothing happened.

THE DELIBERATE DROUGHT

The great difficulty with maintaining an adequate flow of water into the marshlands is that they rely completely on water from the Tigris and Euphrates rivers, both of which headwater in Turkey, and the multiple-year drought in that region had dramatically reduced water levels in both rivers. The worst part of the drought had occurred during 2007 and 2008. By the spring of 2009 rains had returned to the Taurus Mountains, but precipitation was still below average.

In the Tigris, water levels had fallen drastically during 2007 and 2008, but in 2009 the river gradually rose again in response to the increased precipitation. But although the headwaters of the Euphrates also received more rainfall in 2009, that river's flow into Iraq continued to fall throughout the year. The difference between the responses of the two rivers results from the extent to which Turkey controls their flow. The Tigris remains relatively unfettered by dams in Turkey, but the country has a virtual lock on the waters of the Euphrates. The capacity of reservoirs on the Euphrates in Turkey equals three times its annual flow, meaning that theoretically, the country could retain its entire throughput for several years.

Although the water shortage in the marshes of the Euphrates initially resulted from the naturally occurring drought, the shortfall was further exacerbated by Turkey holding excess water in its reservoirs. The water shortage occurred just when the two countries were wrangling over a multitude of issues, including the movement of Kurdish rebel groups across their shared border and the question of whether Iraq would supply natural gas through Turkey's proposed Nabucco pipeline to Europe. Suspicions arose that Turkey was opening and closing its reservoir gates in an effort to influence political negotiations with Iraq.

Before the Ataturk dam was constructed, an average of 1,000 cubic meters per second[12] (cms) flowed into Iraq through the Euphrates, but by the 1990s that amount had been reduced to 600 cms. In April 2009, only 230 cms were trickling through the Euphrates across Iraq's northern border.

TURKEY'S GAP PROJECT

With the flow of water through the Euphrates completely under Turkish control, the one hope for water for the marshlands was from the Tigris River, which also headwaters in the Turkish mountains but had not yet been controlled by dams. But Turkey's GAP project proposed construction of the enormous Ilisu Dam on the Tigris, which would control the waters of the Tigris as securely as those of the Euphrates, leaving Iraq completely at the mercy of Turkey to pass through any water from either river. Turkey had been promised export credits to construct the dam from three European countries—Switzerland, Germany, and Austria. These export credits were due to be finalized in mid-2009.

But many humanitarian and environmental groups oppose the Ilisu Dam, and in May 2009, they convened the Ilisu Summit in Berlin, bringing together activists from Turkey, Iraq, and Europe. Hassan Janabi attended the meeting and forcefully voiced Iraq's opposition to the dam. After the summit, Germany withdrew its support for the Ilisu Dam, effectively killing the export credits as the three countries had agreed to act unanimously. Announcing that it would fund the project through its own financial resources, Turkey broke ground on the project shortly thereafter, predicting completion of the dam by 2015.

[12] One cms is equivalent to 1.3 cubic yards per second or 260 gallons per second

Just before the Ilisu Summit, the Turkish foreign minister had announced his intention to increase the flow through the Euphrates to 515 cms in the near term, and subsequently to 715 cms during July to September 2009. But by early June, the flow into Iraq remained at 230 cms, and Iraq's Ministry of Water Resources formally asked Turkey to make good on its promise and release an additional 500 cms. A few days after Germany withdrew its support for the Ilisu Dam, Iraq reported that the flow of the Euphrates into Iraq had risen to 570 cms. But when all three countries formally withdrew from the project, the flow fell back to 370 cms.

STILL DYING FOR WATER

The searing heat of summer 2009 quickly evaporated what was left in the rivers. Water levels in the Euphrates were so low that power plants in Nasriya could not generate electricity. The markets in Chubayish began selling frozen imported fish. Even snakes fled their natural habitat and created a plague in the nearby cities. Dozens of sandstorms swept through the dried marshes and across Iraq, some of them large enough to span the width of the country. Uncontrolled fires swept through the dried vegetation. Hundreds of marsh dwellers marched in a demonstration in Nasriya to demand action and water, to no avail.

In Baghdad, the MoWR was under increasing pressure to obtain more water. Minister Rashid blasted Turkey for failing to meet its promises, claiming that its reservoirs were full of water that was being deliberately withheld from Iraq. Turkey denied his accusations.

In the fall of 2009, heavy rains returned to Turkey, bringing a devastating flood to Istanbul. Precipitation increased over northern Iraq, improving rain-fed agriculture but shedding little water into the rivers that nourish the downstream marshlands. The drought officially ended, yet most of Iraq remained parched.

MAKING THE MOST OF WHAT YOU HAVE

Winter saw no change in the marshlands. The Chubayish marsh remained dry. The eastern Hammar marshes remained dry. Southern Hawizeh remained dry. The marshes and their people were dying. So once again, activists within CRIM, the Ministry of Environment, the Ramsar National Committee, and Nature Iraq plotted together to find any means of bringing water to the dehydrated marshes.

They realized that a large quantity of water was still being diverted from the marshes of the Euphrates through the Main Outfall Drain (MOD). This canal drains water from the agricultural fields of central Iraq, bypassing the marshlands and discharging it into the Gulf. The Main Outfall Drain benefited the marshlands by diverting this polluted agricultural drainage water.

But desperate times call for desperate measures, and the cadre decided that low quality, polluted water was better than no water at all for the marshes. So the CRIM engineers designed a system that would divert 50% of the MOD water into the Karmashia portion of Hammar Marsh. Construction finished in February 2010 and within a month, the waters from the MOD had flooded more than 10 miles (16 km) into the parched wetland. The quality of the water proved to be better than anticipated, and healthy vegetation soon began to sprout again.

Meanwhile, a year had passed since Nature Iraq first proposed the 7/12 dam project, and nothing had been implemented. Apparently the project had been shelved due to strenuous objections from the towns within the Basra governorate downstream of the proposed dam, which feared that the project could negatively impact their municipal water supply. The original 7/12 dam lay within the Basra governorate, and their Governing Council was the most powerful in the region. But then the activists in Dhi Qar realized that the Basra Council had no authority in their governorate, and they could avoid the need to bargain with them if they simply moved the dam project westward into their own jurisdiction.

So in April 2010 the Dhi Qar governorate constructed an earthen dam spanning the Euphrates; large-diameter pipes placed beneath the embankment allowed water to flow through to the towns downstream. The new dam created the desired effect in the marshlands. West of the dam, water levels rose in the Euphrates so that the level in the river was higher than that in the marshlands. The resulting hydraulic gradient caused water to flow from the Euphrates through the breached embankments and back into the marshes. Within weeks, water began rushing into the parched ground. Through the rest of the summer and fall, water continued to flood the marshes, creeping further and further, about ten miles (16 km) northward into the Chubayish Marsh and fifteen miles (24 km) southward into the Hammar Marsh. Reeds and rushes quickly sprouted in the wetted soil, and by late summer the entire marsh shone verdant green on the new satellite images.

In western Hammar Marsh, the al-Winais clan had stayed on during the drought, determined to maintain their position in their ancestral lands. With the influx of water from the MOD, their lives began again. Likewise, the Baher clan, numbering around 800, had managed to keep their buffaloes alive with water from the Euphrates. In Karmashia, about 500 people remained in their homes on the embankment, fishing and cutting reeds for their survival. In the settlements on the south side of the Chubayish marshes—Abu Subatt, Abu Narsi, Abu Cholaba, Khanzeeri, Sabaghia, and Mwajid— about 50,000 people managed to survive the devastation. And after the wetlands were re-flooded, the Ghadban clan returned to Ishan Hallab, joined by an additional clan of former marsh dwellers who migrated back to Ishan Qubba.

HAWIZEH RAMSAR SITE IN TROUBLE

In the Central and Hammar Marshes, the resilient wetlands and their long-suffering people survived yet another brush with annihilation. But the marshes of Hawizeh—long thought to have the highest values of biodiversity—still suffered. In 2007, both the northern and southern portions of Hawizeh had been designated as a "Wetland of International Importance" through the Ramsar Convention. The conservation community breathed a sigh of relief that at least this fragile remnant of the Mesopotamian Marshlands would have a legal protection.

But southern Hawizeh is underlain by the vast petroleum reserves of the Majnoon oilfields and Iran's Azadegan oilfield occurs just across the border. During the Iran-Iraq war, massive and bloody battles had taken place over the shared marshlands and their subterranean assets. Ramsar status or not, the two countries could be expected to protect and develop their rights to the oil.

As Iraq began to re-flood the wetlands in 2003, Iran began construction of an earthen dyke along the border. For southern Hawizeh there was no significant impact, but northern Hawizeh was suddenly shut off from water flowing in from the Karkheh River to the east. Now northern Hawizeh depended solely on the Tigris for its influx of water.

In Iraq, development of the Majnoon oilfields initially provided an odd protection to the fragile environment. Special units of police guarded the oilfields, and they did not allow any guns or hunters into the area. Somehow the birds seemed to realize that here they were not threatened by humans and their population exploded in southern Hawizeh. In the KBA survey in January 2009, the KBA team found a total of 49 species and over 25,000 individuals at just one single site in the marshland.

By spring 2009, though, southern Hawizeh began to slowly shrink and by the fall of 2009 it had completely disappeared. No official explanation of this desiccation has been provided.

In April 2010, Iraq's Ramsar Committee placed Hawizeh Marsh on the Montreaux Record, acknowledging that the marsh was experiencing serious problems. The Montreaux Record lists those Ramsar wetlands where an adverse change in ecological character has occurred or is likely to occur, and which are therefore in need of priority conservation attention. Iraq's formal petition cited four main causes of degradation: lingering effects from the 1990s drainage; the decrease in rainfall due to global warming; the decrease in water supplies due to upstream damming; and the lack of water-sharing agreements with co-riparian states.

In this case, placement on the Montreaux List did not create urgent action to save the wetlands. Southern Hawizeh remains dry as of mid-2012.

DEATH SENTENCE FOR ENVIRONMENTAL DESTRUCTION

The Supreme Iraqi Criminal Tribunal concluded its trial for the crime of draining of the marshlands in August 2010. Saddam himself had been dead for almost four years, and the primary defendant, Saddam Hussein's cousin Ali Hassan al-Majid ("Chemical Ali") had been hanged nine months previously for his crimes against Iraq's Kurdish population. But punishments were meted out. For their crimes against the marshlands and its inhabitants, Mezban Khader Hadi, a member of the Revolutionary Command Council, was sentenced to death; Abdul Ghani Abdul Ghafoor was sentenced to life imprisonment; former Defense Minister Sultan Hashim received a 15-year sentence, and 28 others received sentences of between

7 and 15 years.

During the trial, witnesses such as Baroness Emma Nicholson spoke passionately of the enormous value of the marshlands and their importance as a global historical symbol and an environmental asset to the world. But no one mentioned the present perilous state of those beloved marshlands. No one spoke of how they had almost just disappeared again, without Saddam Hussein's help. Issues of water-sharing treaties with neighboring countries or petroleum development in the marshlands never arose. Not a single voice ventured to ask for permanent protection of the vital ecosystem. And thus the marshlands remain in their precarious position, eternally subject to the whims and political wrangling of those in power.

14. MARSHLAND MANIFESTO

"Ever the river has risen and brought us the flood, the mayfly floating on the water. On the face of the sun its countenance gazes, then all of a sudden nothing is there."

—The Epic of Gilgamesh (Sumerian, circa 1200 BC)

"The Eden Again Project: Promoting Restoration of the Mesopotamian Marshlands." It was a grand title for the modest program Azzam and I had launched as a husband-and-wife team. We were soon to discover that the hardest task of the program—re-flooding the dried marshlands—required no effort at all from anyone outside of the marshlands. Given a slight opportunity, the people of the marshes re-flooded the damaged land, all on their own. This point cannot be over-emphasized: no outsider ever took down a dam, opened a flood gate, or breached a levee. Re-flooding was a home-grown, spontaneous act of liberation.

A decade later, tens of millions of dollars in international aid have been spent on helping to sustain the marsh dweller's hopes of a revived ecosystem. And still we are left to wonder: did any of these projects achieve any meaningful success? The wetlands are once again wet; formerly dry reeds are green again, rustling in the wind as birds soar across the blue skies above. Marsh dwellers are once again able to pole their slender *mashuf* through the calm waters of the marshlands. But can it truly be said that they have been restored?

FUNCTIONAL RESTORATION

Perhaps, as Dr. Tom Crisman of the University of Florida's Center for Wetlands warned us when we began the project, "restoration" is an unattainable dream: you can never exactly reproduce the conditions of the past.

"You're not God," he told us. "You can't put it back. The best you can hope for is the rehabilitation of an ecosystem. 'Restoration' places paramount importance on a return to the pre-impact condition, which may be largely mythical or even unachievable. For an ecosystem that has been disturbed by humans for millennia, defining which time frame to use as a reference point would be meaningless. Alternatively, the concept of rehabilitation stresses ecosystem functional processes. Rehabilitation asks for what purpose the ecosystem is desired, and then charts a course to achieve that function."

Viewed from that perspective, the marshes are once again performing most of their vital historical functions and providing many of the same environmental services they traditionally afforded. For example, the marshes once again protect the surrounding cities and farms from flooding by providing an area to receive excess water flow. Evaporation in the wetlands ameliorates the local and regional climate by increasing humidity and decreasing air temperatures. Their reed beds deter desertification and reduce the occurrence of dust storms. Since the massive productivity of their vegetation absorbs carbon dioxide—a major greenhouse gas—the marshlands can even be said to fight global warming.

More importantly, the marshlands provide sustenance and significant economic opportunities for its people. Fishing, water buffalo husbandry, and reed collection activities flourish anew within the ecosystem. These activities have allowed the reestablishment of a millennia-old way of life, and traditions once thought to have disappeared off the face of the earth now thrive in the marshes.

Wildlife also thrives. Once again, the marshlands shelter a significant biodiversity, including numerous endemic and endangered species. Several species of birds that were once potentially on the brink of extinction have been discovered living in the restored marshlands.

But the marshlands of Iraq appear to be caught in a never-ending cycle of desiccation and restoration. As of 2012, they cover about half their historical range. Humans attack the marshes and nature adapts; plants go dormant, wildlife migrates elsewhere. But each time the system dies and returns, the resultant landscape is impoverished. Each time the marshlands go dry, fragile yet important components disappear, perhaps never to be seen again. Each time the marshlands are attacked, more clans of marsh dwellers immigrate to the cities.

At some point, they may never return. All living beings, including humans, need and deserve security in their environment. Attaining it in the marshlands will require a concerted and determined effort on the part of individuals and government institutions both within and surrounding Iraq.

WHAT THE INTERNATIONAL COMMUNITY NEEDS TO DO

The marshlands' most urgent need is a dependable supply of fresh water. This can only be obtained through a negotiated treaty between the co-riparian states of the Tigris and Euphrates—Turkey, Syria, and Iraq—and of the shared waters between Iraq and Iran. Downstream countries of the Gulf, including Kuwait, should be included in these negotiations. The goal of these agreements should be basin-wide management that benefits all parties.

In 2001, UNEP began a comprehensive study of the watershed of the Tigris and Euphrates Rivers. Hassan Partow's report on the Mesopotamian Marshlands was intended as the first step of the study, but the remainder of the work was never completed. UNEP should be supported to complete this program, because data and evaluations presented by an objective third party are desperately needed to provide a framework for any basin-wide agreement.

WHAT IRAQ NEEDS TO DO

The main burden of action lies with Iraq. There are a number of steps it can take to increase the availability of water throughout the country using only the existing water supply. The greatest opportunity for water conservation lies within the agricultural realm. Iraqi farmers are still using the ancient Sumerian technology of flood irrigation for grain production. Before the era of dams, that method was sustainable as the natural floods periodically cleared the salty crust that accumulates from over-irrigation. But now that the rivers are dammed, those types of floods will never happen again. Soil salinization has ruined many agricultural fields in Iraq, and desertification of large swaths of southern Iraq remains a potential threat.

The Iraqi farmer must change from flood irrigation to more

modern methods such as drip irrigation, subterranean irrigation, and spray irrigation. In turn, the Iraqi government must work on modernizing water delivery to farms and improving its water management systems—for example, lining irrigation canals with concrete to reduce loss through infiltration. There should be a national strategy to encourage the replacement of cereal production with vegetable and fruit farming, which uses less water and generates several harvests per year. The Iraqi farmer could then become the supplier of green goods to the local region without having to compete with international farmers who can produce wheat and rice more cheaply.

Oil production in Iraq's southern oil fields will also require the infusion of fresh water in order to maintain adequate pressure. To avoid using precious supplies from the Tigris and Euphrates, Iraq's Oil Ministry has asked a consortium of foreign oil companies to construct one of the largest desalination plants in the world. The estimated $10 billion Common Seawater Supply Facility is intended to process 15 million barrels a day to provide treated water to the southern oil fields. The facility represents an enormous investment, but Iraq must remain firm in its decision not to use its dwindling supplies of fresh surface water to facilitate petroleum production.

Beyond the issue of the quantity of water available for marshland restoration, the timing of water release is also vitally important to the maintenance of a flourishing ecosystem. The country's need for electricity remains relatively stable throughout the year, resulting in a continuous, uniform release of water through dams equipped to generate hydroelectric power. But irrigation needs are highest during the summer, leading to increased water flow during what is naturally the driest part of the year. For the marshlands, one of the key criteria for operation is to attempt to mimic the natural spring flood pulse. This would necessitate a release of water during the early spring, mirroring the natural increase of flow as snow begins to melt in the northern mountains. The flood pulse is an important component of the natural system of the marsh. Environmental needs for water, both in terms of quantity and timing, should be taken into consideration in the operation of Iraq's extensive river control system. At present, the Ministry of Water Resources meets regularly with the Ministry of Electricity and the Ministry of Agriculture to determine their estimated operating needs for the upcoming period. The Ministry of the Environment should be included in these meetings as well.

The people of the south—the marsh dwellers and surrounding people who utilize the marshlands for fishing and hunting—also

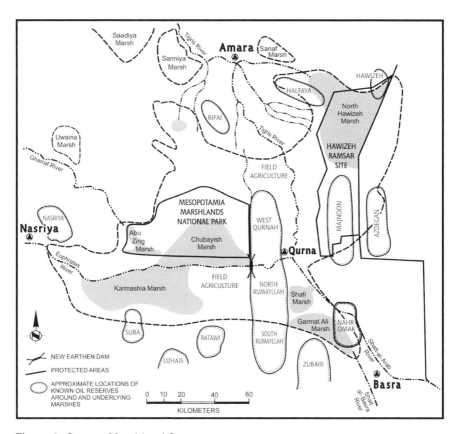

Figure 9. Current Marshland Status

have difficult decisions to make. Given the constraints of water quantity, 100% of the marshlands cannot be sustainably restored. Full restoration is a laudable goal, but robust restoration of a smaller portion of the marshlands is preferable to a more widespread project that does not provide the valuable functions required of the ecosystem.

How to decide which areas to restore and which to leave dry or convert to another beneficial use? Most of the areas that have been restored in the last decade were re-flooded through the independent actions of the local people, who have spoken with their deeds: they want marshlands. The footprint of recent re-flooding can easily be used as a blueprint for future restoration.

Some areas of the dried marshes have been successfully converted to field agriculture. The inhabitants of these areas apparently wish to continue in the farming lifestyle, so such areas could be excluded from restoration plans. But it must be emphasized, however, that most of the marshlands area is not suitable for cereal cultivation because the soils have too much salt and too little drainage. The most economically-viable crop are the reedbeds and the economic activities that they support—fishing, dairy production, reed handicrafts, and potentially also poultry feed, paper products, and ecotourism.

Much of southern Iraq's petroleum reserves underlie the former marshlands. While wetlands can, and have been, restored and successfully maintained within operating oilfields, the exclusion of existing and planned oilfields from wetlands restoration makes common sense. The North Rumaila field, currently operated by British Petroleum and the China National Petroleum Corporation, occupies the south-central portion of Hammar Marsh. The perimeter of the oilfield is currently dyked and guarded. The West Qurna oilfield, to be operated by ExxonMobil and Royal Dutch Shell, extends north of Rumaila and into the southeastern portion of the Central Marshes. Much of the West Qurna oilfield is also dyked and guarded. The Majnoon oilfield, to be operated by Royal Dutch Shell and Malaysia's Petronas, is located in south Hawizeh. This area had been re-flooded in 2004 and subsequently harbored a magnificent abundance of migratory waterfowl, but it was dyked and re-drained in 2009, apparently to allow for development of those oil resources. In an area as vast as the Mesopotamian marshlands, the footprint of these fields can easily be interwoven with other economic projects along with environmental restoration.

Areas that should be included in the restoration plan include North Hawizeh, which has never been dried and retains the highest ecological values, along with areas that have been purposefully re-flooded by the local inhabitants. These latter areas include the Abu Zirig, Chubayish, Auda, Karmashia, Shafi, and Garmat Ali areas of the Central and Hammar marshes. The inhabitants of these areas have made their wishes clear—so clear that they can be observed by satellites orbiting the earth. Those wishes must be respected. Of course, there may be a few families within those areas who do not want their land flooded; such issues should be resolved through local negotiations. More problematic are those tribes that wish to have their local marshes restored but have not been able to re-flood them on their own. Great disappointment and resistance may be encountered when explaining that their local marshes may never be slated for restoration.

Continued implementation of an uncoordinated decision-making process could result in a patchwork of isolated marshes only loosely connected to each other. Some of the areas that have been re-flooded still suffer from poor water quality, such as the Chubayish marsh. Other areas, such as Karmashia marsh, have no outlet—water flows in, ponds, and evaporates, leaving behind ever more salt until the area will eventually become a saltwater marsh. It is imperative, therefore, that adequate and reliable water be supplied to all of these marshes, and that hydraulic connections and hydraulic flow-through be established between the individual marshes, the twin rivers, and the Gulf.

Detailed ecological work should continue, allowing for restoration not only of marshland vegetation but also of native wildlife—fish, birds, and mammals such as the Smooth-coated Otter and the Jungle Cat, for example. As security allows, international experts on wetlands and wildlife should be brought in to consult on how best to achieve the maximum ecological value and functions from these wetlands systems. Preservation of wildlife and biodiversity while respecting traditional human usage of the marshland resources may prove to be a difficult matter but surely the outcome will prove the effort worthwhile.

The Iraqi government also needs to develop a systematic land tenure system whereby the areas slated for environmental conservation can be legally protected. The two areas requiring immediate and meaningful legal protections are the Ramsar site in Hawizeh Marsh and the National Park site in the Central Marshes.

The national and local government ministries should continue to focus on providing basic social services to the marshlands—health, education, transportation, and communication—within the context of environmental conservation. Economic opportunities in the marshlands should be aimed toward increasing the profit made by harvesting the marshlands' natural resources. For example, instead of simply producing buffalo milk, milk processing plants constructed in the larger villages of the marshlands could increase their revenue stream. Instead of merely catching fish, a fish processing plant could similarly provide much-needed local jobs.

In the future, security will improve and tourists will come. An effort should be made to resurrect and preserve handcrafting skills that might otherwise be lost. The sale of high-quality products, woven from marshland plants or cast from its mud, could be an important source of income for the local men and women. Brightly-colored rugs, hand-woven from local wool, are also a specialty and could potentially fetch high prices.

WHAT YOU CAN DO

Support Nature Iraq. Visit their website at www.natureiraq.org and learn more about their activities and the current status of Iraq's environment, including the marshlands. The "Get Involved" section of the website includes a list of equipment desired by the scientists and information on how to donate money. Become a member. Nature Iraq also has some items for sale, including its own publications, sets of greeting cards featuring marshland scenes, and Nature Iraq shirts and caps. Volunteer positions are also available— some activities, such as editing, translation or grant writing, could be done from your own country of residence, but Nature Iraq's office in Sulaymania occasionally offers in-country internships for persons with specialized expertise pertinent to their work.

Get others involved. Have your local charity organization sponsor an event to raise money; Nature Iraq will try to provide a speaker. Or design your own program to support a specific project in the marshlands in conjunction with Nature Iraq or another group active in the area.

Help publicize this book's message of hope. Suggest it to your book club, ask your local library or bookstore to carry it, review the book in your blog, ask your local newspaper to write a review, and lend your copy to friends.

Support equitable and just water sharing in the region. In 2009,

Germany, Switzerland and Austria withdrew their financial backing for the Ilisu Dam, due in part to lobbying from their own citizens along with international environmental and human rights groups. Lobby any pertinent government or organization to oppose Ilisu Dam until an equitable water sharing treaty has been signed between the nations that share the waters of the Tigris and Euphrates Rivers.

Lobby the major international oil companies working in the former marshlands—at present writing, these include British Petroleum, ExxonMobil, and Royal Dutch Shell—to support local ecosystem restoration, renewable sources of oilfield injection water, and sustainable development projects for improving the socioeconomic lives of the marsh dwellers in keeping with their traditions and natural environment.

Make plans to visit the Mesopotamian Marshlands. In 2009 a group of intrepid westerners successfully completed a tour of Iraq, including the area near the marshlands. The National Park is intended to serve as a locus for ecotourism, and Nature Iraq and the Ministry of the Environment have recently built a *mudhif* at the entrance of the park to serve as a rest stop for anticipated eco-cultural tourists in the near future.

From there, visitors can board a native *mashuf*, and listen to the languid slap of water against the side of the slim canoe as they are poled through the dense thicket of reeds, watching in wonder as flocks of migrating birds trail through the indigo skies above. Entering an open-water lake dotted with reed huts on individual man-made islands, they can smell the dusky smoke of dung fires as the marsh dwellers prepare their noon meal of *masgouf* and wild herbs. Basking in the warmth of the sun and the generous hospitality of the local people, their senses filled with a garden of earthly delights, these travelers will find themselves transported through the millennia, finally experiencing the satisfaction of a healthy and abundant relationship between humans and their natural environment.

GOING HOME TO EDEN AGAIN

Hopefully these visitors, along with our readers, will return home to gaze at their own local habitat from a new perspective. Because no matter how impoverished or abused that environment may be, it can be restored. Nature is resilient. If the Mesopotamian Marshlands can be resurrected so many times from so many deaths, then perhaps any environment can be reborn.

For Eden is not a place but an ideal. It lies not on a map but in the human awareness and appreciation of our wondrous natural surroundings, in our affinity with the living universe. Paradise happens when we are at peace within nature. If we can somehow heal our land and rescue our fellow creatures on this planet, then we can heal our souls and emerge ourselves reborn.

And we can find Eden again.

ACKNOWLEDGEMENTS

This book could not have been written without the assistance of Azzam Alwash, who undertook the difficult work in Iraq to make our vision of a restored ecosystem a reality. I give a million thanks to all of the Nature Iraq staff. Those scientists and engineers, cooks and drivers, guides and boatmen, managers and technicians all readily gave me everything I needed and made me feel welcomed each time I visited, in Chubayish, Baghdad, and Sulaymania. Special thanks go to Jassim Asadi, who made everything happen: he is a true prince of the marshes.

I thank all of my sources named in the volume: they are the ones who made the miracles happen both in and outside of Iraq. It humbles me to be able to tell their stories and I hope that I have done them justice. I remain profoundly grateful that I was allowed to play a small role in helping them achieve the miracle of rebirth in the marshes. I realize that I have left hundreds of tales untold; I hope that someday all of the heroes of the marshes will be recognized.

My most heartfelt gratitude goes to the warm people of Chubayish (especially Abu Abbas al-Asadi) and to the marsh dwellers who took me into their homes and willingly shared their stories: I hope the world listens to your tales and reaches out to you as you did to me. My days with you were few yet will forever remain vividly in my memory as some of the highlights of my life. Your kindness, generosity, and exuberant spirit touched my soul.

This book was written over the course of five long years, and without the support of my friends and family I would never have finished. Susan Aluzri, Khalid Alwan, Liana Hernandez, Donn Gorsline, and Jeff Newland read early drafts of the manuscript and provided helpful viewpoints and insights. Technical experts graciously reviewed some of the chapters: Richard Porter (birds), Brian Coad (fish), Andrea Cattarossi (water), Hassan Janabi (water and recommendations) and Jennifer Pournelle (ancient history).

Richard Balkin served as my agent for a portion of this long process and gave me much-needed practical advice on the work—I appreciate your effort. Robin Swados provided expert and generous copy-editing. Evan Franson checked facts. Stephanie Richardson drafted the figures, Charlie Clark of Elegance Printing lent invaluable advice and patience, and Tania Baban-Natal created the beautiful interior design and cover.

A special thanks to my daughters Hannah and Norah, who always supported my efforts in writing this book and never expressed the doubts that I am sure they harbored: you fill my life with joy.

And above all: I lift my voice in praise to our loving God who blessed me with this opportunity to serve his creation.

☙ SELECTED BIBLIOGRAPHY

Marsh Dweller Culture, Anthropology, and Ethnography

Anthropology of Iraq, Part 1 no. 2: The Lower Euphrates-Tigris Delta by Henry Field (1949) Chicago Natural History Museum, 412p.

Marsh Dwellers of the Euphrates Delta by Shakir Mustafa Salim (1962) University of London, 157p.

Guests of the Sheikh by Elizabeth Warnock Fernea (1965) Doubleday, New York, 346pp.

The Marsh Dwellers of Southern Iraq: Their Habitat, Origins, Society, and Economy by Albertine Jwaideh (2007) University of Toronto, 40p.

The Marshes in the 20th Century

The Marsh Arab: Haji Rikkan by Fulanain (1928) Lippencott, 323p.

People of the Reeds by Gavin Maxwell (1957) Harper Brothers, New York, 224p. (published in England under the title A Reed Shaken by the Wind.)

Marsh Dwellers of Southern Iraq by Wilfred Thesiger and Gavin Maxwell (1958) National Geographic Magazine, v. 113, no. 2, p. 205-239.

The Marsh Arabs by Wilfred Thesiger (1964) Butler and Tanner, London, 242p.

Water Dwellers in a Desert World by Gavin Young and Nik Wheeler (1976) National Geographic Magazine, v. 149 no. 4, p.502-523.

Return to the Marshes by Gavin Young (1977) Collins, London, 224p.

Der Tigris des alten Mesopotamien, Iraq by Ursula Schulz-Dornburg und F. Rudolf Knubel (1980) Kestner-Gesellschaft Hannover, 90p.

The Desiccation of the Marshes

The Longest War: The Iran-Iraq Conflict by Dilip Hiro (1990) Routledge, 323p.

The Estimation of Marshland Degradation in Southern Iraq using Multitemporal Landsat TM Images by Munro, D.C. and H. Touron (1997) International Journal of Remote Sensing, v. 18 no. 7, p. 1597-1606.

Republic of Fear: The Politics of Modern Iraq by Kanan Makiya (originally published under the pseudonym Samir al-Khalili) (1998) University of California Press, 323p.

The Environmental Legacy of Saddam Husayn: the Archaeology of Totalitarianism in Modern Iraq by Alexander H. Joffe (2000) in Crime, Law, and Social Change v. 33 no. 4, p. 313-328.

The Mesopotamian Marshlands: Demise of an Ecosystem by Hassan Partow (2001) United Nations Environmental Program, 46p.

Shatt Al Arab River Marshes Drainage by Hanan Ramzy (2001) Kuwait Institute for Scientific Research, 21p.

The Iraqi Government Assault on the Marsh Arabs (2003) Human Rights Watch, 16p.

An Environmental and Ecological Study of the Marshlands of Mesopotamia, AMAR Appeal (1994), 200p.

The Iraqi Marshlands: A Human and Environmental Study edited by Emma Nicholson and Peter Clark (2002) Politico's Publishing, 332p.

Wetlands of Mass Destruction; Ancient Presage for Contemporary Ecocide in Southern Iraq Edited by Robert France (2007) Green Frigate Books, 248p.

Monitoring and Assessment Programme of Shatt al-Arab and the Iraqi Coastal Waters, Regional Environmental Remediation Advisory Group (2008) Marine Science Center, University of Basrah, 33p.

Ancient History in the Marshes

History Begins at Sumer (3rd Edition) by Samuel Noah Kramer (1981) University of Pennsylvania Press, 388p.

The Sumerians: Their History, Culture, and Character by Samuel Noah Kramer (1963) University of Chicago Press, 355p.

Ancient Iraq (3rd Edition) by Georges Roux (1992) Pelican Books, 547p.

Early Mesopotamia: Society and Economy at the Dawn of History by J.N. Postgate (1992) Routledge Publishers, 367p.

Daily Life in Ancient Mesopotamia by Karen Rhea Nemet-Nejat (1998) Greenwood Press, 346p.

Treasures from the Royal Tombs of Ur edited by Richard Zettler and Lee Horne (1998) University of Pennsylvania Museum of Archaeology and Anthropology, 195p.

Mesopotamia: The Invention of the City by Gwendolyn Leick (2002) Penguin Group, 360p.

Iraq's Marsh Arabs in the Garden of Eden by Edward Ochsenschlager (2004) University of Pennsylvania Museum of Archaeology and Anthropology, 285p.

Marshland of Cities: Deltaic Landscapes and Mesopotamian Civilization (2003) by Jennifer Pournelle, PhD Dissertation, University of California at San Diego.

Post-War Recovery of the Marshes

United Nations Inter-agency Assessment of Vulnerable Groups, Part I: Marsh Arabs (2003) International Organization on Migration, 6p.

Building a Scientific Basis for Restoration of the Mesopotamian Marshlands (2003) by International Technical Advisory Panel Restoration Planning Workshop Convened by the Eden Again Project, Iraq Foundation, 67p.

The New Eden Project: Final Report by the Italian Ministry of the Environment and Territory and the Free Iraq Foundation (2004) 231p.

Iraq Marshlands Restoration Program Action Plan (2004) FORWARD Task Order, Water Indefinite Quantity Contract U.S. A.I.D., 230p

The Restoration Potential of the Mesopotamian Marshes of Iraq by Richardson, C., Reiss, P., Hussain, N., Alwash, A. and Pool, D. (2005) Science v. 307 p. 1307-1311 plus appendices.

New Eden Master Plan for Integrated Water Resources Management in the Marshlands Area by the Italian Ministry of the Environment and Territory, the Free Iraq Foundation, and Nature Iraq (2006) The New Eden Group, 1600p.

Iraq Marshlands Restoration Program – Final Report (2006) U.S. Agency for International Development, 192p

Iraqi Marshlands Observation System Technical Report by United Nations Environmental Program (2007) 71p.

Iraq and Iran in Ecological Perspective: The Mesopotamian Marshes and the Hawizeh-Azim Peace Park by Michelle Stevens (2007) in Peace Parks: Conservation and Conflict Resolution, MIT Press.

Management Plan for the Hawizeh Marsh Ramsar Site of Iraq by the Iraq National Marshlands and Wetlands Committee (2008) Office of the Prime Minister of Iraq, 51p.

Physical History and Conditions in the Marshes

Recent Sediments of the Tigris-Euphrates Delta: Southern Marshes (Ahwar) by Aqrawri, A.A.M. (1993) PhD. Dissertation, University of London Imperial College.

Climate of Iraq (2004) U.S. National Climate Data Center, available online at: **http://www.ncdc.noaa.gov/oa/climate/afghan/iraq-narrative.html**

Ecology of the Marshes

Euphrates and Tigris, Mesopotamian Ecology and Destiny by Julian Rzóska (1980) Monographiae Biologicae vol. 38, 122 pp.

Children's Bird Guide of Iraq (2007) M. Salim. & A.F. Omar, with Kurdish translation by K. Ararat & R. Rashed, Nature Iraq, 50p. [in Arabic]

Freshwater Fishes of Iraq by Brian Coad (2010) PenSoft, Sofia-Moscow, 274p.

KBA Summary Report 2004-2008: Objectives and Scope by Nature Iraq (2009) Nature Iraq, Sulaymania, Iraq, 27pp.

KBA South Site Review 2008 by Nature Iraq (2009) Nature Iraq, Sulaymania, Iraq, 79p.

Field Guide to the Birds of Iraq by Salim, MA, Porter, RF, Schiermacker-Hansen, P, Christensen S & Al-Jbour, S. (2006) Nature Iraq/BirdLife International, Baghdad, 252p [In Arabic]

An annotated checklist of the birds of Iraq by Salim, M, Al-Sheikhly, OF, Ararat, K & Porter RF (2012) Sandgrouse 34 (1), p 4-43.

Important Bird Areas in the Middle East compiled by MI Evans (1994) BirdLife International, 410p

A Directory of Wetlands in the Middle East compiled by Derek A Scott (1995) IUCN & IWRB, 559p.

Water Resources and the Marshes

The Regime of the Rivers Euphrates and Tigris by M.G. Ionides (1937) Chemical Publishing Company of New York, 212p.

Report on the Control of the Rivers of Iraq and the Utilization of their Waters by F.F. Haigh, President of the Irrigation Development Commission (1951). Baghdad Press, 182p.

The Groundwater Geology of Iraq by James Holwerda (1958) PhD Dissertation, University of Southern California, 177p.

Hydrological Survey of Iraq by Harza Engineering and Binnie & Partners (1963), 300+p.

Miscellaneous

Delights from the Garden of Eden: A Cookbook and History of the Iraqi Cuisine by Nawal Nasrallah (2003) Nawal Nasrallah, 646p.

Ring of Bright Water by Gavin Maxwell (1961) Penguin, 211p.

PHOTOGRAPH CREDITS

Mudhafar Salim: 2, 5, 6, 9, 10, 12, 17, 19, 21, 23, 24
Omar Fadil: 20, 22, 31
Azzam Alwash: 11, 13, 14, 15, 27, 30
Suzanne Alwash: 4, 7, 25, 26
Nature Iraq staff: 1, 3, 8, 16, 18, 28, 29, 32